KIRKWALL HARBOUR, Orkney : J CAMPBELL KERR

Under The Eaves

BENEATH the roof, in the keen, biting air,
My friends, the birds, are nesting there.
Carrying twigs, and grasses and leaves,
To build a home — just under the eaves.

Under a window, in early spring,
I watch them work, as they fly out and in.
Parents to be — with what delicate ease,
They build for a family — under the eaves.

If I could build a nest complete,
From twigs and leaves and grass at my feet,
If I could work with such skill and care,
As these twittering creatures — the birds of the air,
I'd think myself clever, but only to these,
God gave the sure knowledge — to build under eaves.

— *Margaret M. Dixon.*

4

People's Friend Annual

•

CONTENTS

BACK COVER Threave Castle, Dumfries

"I SHOULD be away for about an hour." Forbes Malcolm paused in the doorway of his fishing shop and spoke to his assistant. "I'll be back in time to let you go for your usual lunch-hour."

Carefully, he carried out a new salmon rod, well protected in a spotless canvas container, and placed it on the seat of his elderly car. He eased himself into the driving seat and moved off.

His destination was a farm located about two miles from Inveraber, the market town where he had lived and worked all his thirty-four years.

IF ONLY SHE'D

He drove steadily down the country road, humming gently under his breath and contemplating what stock he should take to the game fair which was being held on a large estate near Inveraber the following week.

Suddenly the car lurched violently to one side. It took all Forbes' concentration and strength to grip the steering-wheel and hold it straight and steady. Gradually, he pulled to a halt.

The puncture to the nearside front wheel came as no surprise but

by MARIE WEIR

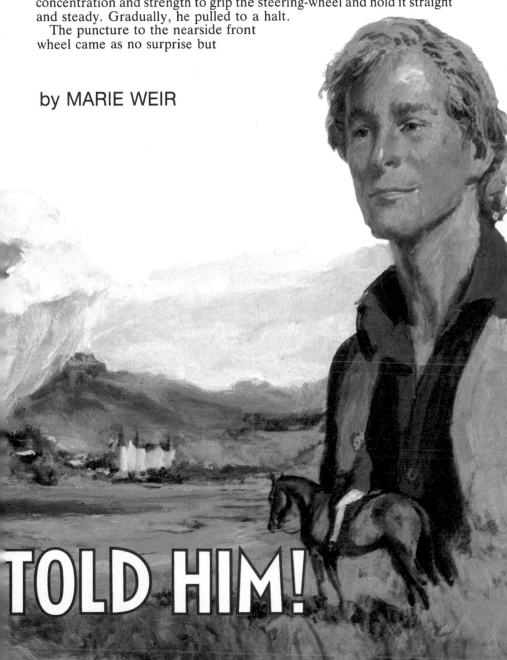

TOLD HIM!

Forbes gave an exclamation of annoyance as he surveyed the offending tyre. Impatiently he set about changing the wheel.

He was tightening the last nut when he became aware of a small, blue car pulling up directly behind him. A girl got out and came towards him.

Forbes straightened up as she approached. She was tall and slim with shoulder-length hair and friendly grey-green eyes.

"Looks as if you've fixed everything now," she commented, sliding her hands into the pockets of her jeans.

"It was just a puncture," Forbes responded. "Thanks for stopping all the same, it was very kind of you."

He ran a hand through his already rough fair hair leaving a smudge of dirt on his cheek, giving him an endearing little-boy look.

"Goodbye and thanks again," Forbes called after her as he watched her retreating figure. She was an interesting girl, he thought.

The little car disappeared round the corner of the narrow road and Forbes was left with a feeling of wonder that someone had felt enough concern for his predicament to stop and offer help. Nowadays he found people kind enough but casual and he had grown used to doing everything for himself and solving his own problems.

Not since his young wife had died all that time ago in the first year of their marriage could he remember a feeling similar to that roused by this girl. Thoughtfully he pulled away from the verge and continued his journey to the farm.

The first thing he saw as he rounded the corner of the steading was the same little blue car.

"Hi, Forbes, we're over here," Harry Graham, the young farmer, called from the direction of the steading. "Come and join us."

Forbes picked up the fishing rod, straightened the tweed jacket that had seen better days, patted his unruly hair with one hand and strode across the yard.

He peered into the gloom of the nearest loose box. Silhouetted against the darkness of the back wall he made out the shape of a horse. As his eyes became accustomed to the shadow he could see a grey stallion with a silver mane and a silver, flowing tail.

Even to his inexpert eyes he could recognise that this was a magnificent animal. He caught a glint of wildness in the horse's faintly-rolling eyes and flared nostrils and would have stepped back instinctively had not Harry Graham spoken.

"Hello, Forbes," he said, "you're just in time to see my latest acquisition. Isn't he a beauty? The Silver King . . . and how he lives up to his name! But I'm calling him Silver for short."

Forbes relaxed as he noticed Silver's head was safely encased in a halter held by Harry.

"He is very handsome although he seems to be a little fierce," Forbes said.

"Nonsense!" Harry Graham dismissed the idea. "He's a proud beauty. All the better for a show of spirit."

Then Forbes noticed the girl — the girl who had stopped to try to help him.

If Only She'd Told Him!

S HE was leaning against the wall nonchalantly enough but she was studying the horse so intently that Forbes realised she was unaware of his presence.

"Harry," she breathed, "he is truly magnificent. I simply can't wait to make a start."

Harry Graham laughed. He was a tall, handsome man, younger than Forbes, with an easy relaxed manner and a ready smile. He had inherited a lucrative estate when his father had died suddenly and now he was able to indulge his hobbies of riding and fishing.

"Carol Campbell," he said mockingly, "I do believe you are more interested in a horse on canvas than you are in a real live one!"

"You're right." She tilted her head to look at him. "I am! In fact, I'll fetch my painting stuff from the car now if you will put him into the paddock. I must study all the different shades of colour in his coat in the full daylight so I can capture them. You are a beauty, Silver."

She leaned forward to stroke the horse's nose but he backed away, startled, and tossed his head.

"Whoa there, you're all right, Silver." Harry pulled the halter gently, his tone reassuring. "He's probably still a bit strange," he explained. "I only collected him last night."

For the first time the girl turned to Forbes.

"You're the man who had the puncture!" she exclaimed.

"You two have met, have you?" Harry intervened.

"Yes, but we don't know each other properly, do we?" Carol moved out of the loose box.

"Let me introduce you then." Harry followed her, leading Silver. "Carol Campbell, this is Forbes Malcolm who is not only the best fisherman in the district . . . and beyond . . . but is the best teacher of casting. He also has a cornucopia of fishing tackle in that shop of his in the High Street in Inveraber."

Forbes and Carol shook hands rather formally as Harry continued.

"Let me just take this fellow into the paddock then we can chat."

Forbes waited as Harry turned Silver loose and Carol rummaged in the back of her car.

"Carol is going to paint a portrait of Silver," Harry explained, and put his arm intimately round her shoulders.

Forbes stood by, silently witnessing this show of affection. Harry seemed to sense the other man's isolation and he quickly turned to Forbes and said:

"Let me see the fishing rod then."

Forbes handed over the canvas-clad rod and immediately the two men became engrossed in talk of rods and lines and reels and flies and fish. Yet, all the time Forbes was aware of Carol's presence.

She had a magnetism that attracted him even although they had only just met. She listened to their talk for some time then she gently put her hand on Harry Graham's arm.

"I'm sorry to interrupt but I think I'll have to go now."

"Right," Harry replied at once. "I'll come with you."

He turned to Forbes.

9

"Thanks very much, Forbes. It was good of you to come personally with the rod. I'll let you know how I get on with it."

Forbes found himself with no option but to leave.

"I'll see you at the game fair," Harry called as Forbes got into his car and drove away.

He turned back to Carol.

"You'll be coming to the game fair, too, won't you?" Harry enquired, then added, "What about coming with me? You could keep me company. Evelyn can't manage to get away that day."

"The trouble with you, Harry Graham, is that you can't go anywhere without a girl in tow!" Carol teased him. "I remember when we were all small and when all the cousins gathered at Auntie Jean's house on a Sunday and we played hide-and-seek, do you remember? And you hated to go off to hide on your own . . . you were always dragging me along with you."

Carol laughed and hugged Harry's arm. "Not that I minded! You and I have always been great friends, haven't we?"

"We certainly have!" Harry squeezed her hand affectionately. "But you still haven't said you'd come with me to the game fair, so . . . ?"

"I'll be there anyway," Carol told him. "I've rented a stall for the first time, so you can come and help sell my pictures. Then Evelyn will know that she need have no qualms about what you're doing as you'll be fully occupied."

"Yes, I'd like to do that." Harry tucked the fishing rod under his arm and began to walk towards the steading. "I'm glad you're taking a stall. You're a very good artist, you know, and I'm proud to call myself your cousin."

THE day before the game fair was due to open Forbes was up early. There was so much to do. The morning was chilly but dry and frost-tinged with a clear sun giving strong indications of a day of sunshine and the promise of another good spell the following day.

Forbes had loaded his car and a trailer with all the stock he wanted to arrange in the stall he had been allocated. The site was in the main block of stalls and therefore should be in a position to attract plenty of attention.

Forbes had had plenty of experience of game fairs as he not only took a stall but he was invariably invited to give casting lessons. However, when he arrived at the big estate, he was in for a shock, His stall was already occupied. He reached back into the car to re-check the plan he'd been sent but there was no mistake. His space had been taken.

He strode into the stall. It was full of drawings and paintings of horses and dogs and there, behind a table sat Carol Campbell.

She looked up.

"Oh, hello," she said, "it's Forbes, Forbes Malcolm, isn't it?"

She smiled but Forbes was in no mood to be charmed, even by her.

"I have to tell you that you have taken my space." He stood tall before her. He was going to spread out the plan on her table but stopped abruptly as she exclaimed:

"No, no, don't put it down there. Can't you see there is a painting there already?"

Forbes apologised briefly. He held the map in mid-air and jabbed at it with a finger. "I was allocated space number twenty-five and this is it."

"That's strange," she returned, "because I, too, was allocated space number twenty-five . . . and I'm in it!" Her smile had vanished at the tone of his voice.

They glared at each other, each obstinately entrenched in a position of being "right."

Forbes broke the silence.

"I'll go to see Colonel Macdonald. He made the stall allocations so he can sort this out."

Moments Musical

THE music moves in mystic melody
Mellifluous tones make magic on the air.
The crashing chords resound in majesty,
Then fade to murmurous sighs of silent prayer.

The deep sonorous sounds in harmony,
That seem to heal one's hurt and gently bless,
Come forth from voice and strings in unity
And hold a haunting hint of holiness.
— Margaret Comer.

"I don't think there is much to sort out," Carol retorted. "I was allocated this space and I'm using it."

"Possession being nine-tenths of the law, I suppose," Forbes sneered.

As he spoke he could hardly believe his ears. He prided himself on being equable and affable, always ready to find a compromise. Now he hardly understood this swift anger or the way he was expressing it.

Forbes clenched his teeth and marched off to find Colonel Macdonald. The administrator examined all his papers then raised his head.

"I can only say I'm very sorry, Mr Malcolm," he began.

"You mean you've made a mistake and you've double-booked that space?" Forbes allowed his anger to show.

"What can I say, except that I apologise most sincerely," repeated the colonel.

"And what do you expect me to do? That was an excellent site . . . I don't suppose there is another one available that is so good. Do you realise I stand to lose a considerable amount of money? It's my living we're talking about."

"Yes, I know, but we can hardly ask Miss Campbell to move now when she has arranged all her paintings, can we?" The colonel tried to placate. "In fact, I can give you a very good site down by the river which would be more convenient as it is much nearer to your teaching position. That area will attract a lot of people, you know."

Forbes felt there was little more he could do but accept the colonel's offer. He walked slowly back to his car. Carol was standing outside the stall.

"Well?" she queried as he came along. "What's the colonel's decision?"

"The space was double-booked by Colonel Macdonald but I'm the one who has to move," Forbes muttered ungraciously.

"Thank you very much, that's good of you." Carol's smile half returned but Forbes was not in a mood to be beguiled.

"I didn't have much choice, did I?" he retorted as he climbed into the car, slammed the door and drove off.

FORBES was so busy for the rest of that day that his irritation and frustration concerning Carol Campbell died away. When the game fair opened his new site proved to be so popular that he had more business than he could easily cope with.

In the late afternoon there was a lull so he walked over to Carol's stall. He stopped to look inside but a different lady was sitting at the table. He took the opportunity to study the paintings. He was impressed. Carol was no mean artist. The life-like appearance of the horses in particular showed not only great technical ability but a focus on detail that made the end product so distinctive.

She must spend considerable time with each subject to reach such perfection, he thought, and later, his admiration for her work was bolstered by one of his own elderly customers.

"I'll just show this to you," the old man told him. "Blackie, my Labrador, is an old man now, like his master and maybe not long for this world. So I wanted to have a painting of him. It was that young lass Carol Campbell who did it."

The old man held out the canvas admiringly.

"It's very good," Forbes said, and again he wished he could speak to Carol and apologise for his behaviour.

"Ay, well, it means a lot to me," the old man went on. "We've come through a lot together, Blackie and I. He's been a faithful friend and I wanted to have a keepsake of him. This is him to the life. I'm very pleased with it."

"Carol Campbell has got talent, hasn't she?" Forbes' reply was more rhetorical than seeking a response.

★　　　★　　　★　　　★

When the game fair ended and the clearing up had been almost completed Forbes again went over to Carol's space. He was uncertain what he was going to say or do, he only knew that he must see her again and put matters right between them.

All at once, he stopped short. There she was, surrounded by packing cases but she was not alone. Harry Graham was at her side and they were talking together, their heads close.

For a moment Forbes watched them with a feeling of hopelessness. Carol Campbell, attractive, animated and talented was not for him. He moved away disconsolately.

A few days later, Harry Graham came into the fishing shop.

"Good morning, Forbes," he said. "I was passing and I wanted to see

If Only She'd Told Him!

you for two reasons. Firstly, I'm delighted with my salmon rod. It has the right balance and my casting seems to have improved since I got it."

Forbes smiled. "I'm glad you're satisfied with it," he said quietly.

"Right," Harry continued, "and the second thing is that I'd like to buy a good, little rod for a lady. I want your advice and I'll take any rod you recommend."

"Well," Forbes replied thoughtfully, "I don't think I've got such a rod in stock but I can easily get one for you by the day after tomorrow."

"You do just that." Harry turned towards the door.

"I'll deliver it to the farm whenever it comes in," Forbes offered.

"Now that would be good of you because it is to be a birthday present and I need to have it as quickly as possible." Harry paused then added, "I'll be away when you deliver it but perhaps you'd just hand it into the house."

Consequently, Forbes found himself driving towards the Graham farm again with another new rod beside him. He had chosen it with particular care as he imagined it was going to be a present for Carol Campbell.

Harry Graham would certainly want her to learn to fish. He was disappointed that there would be a little chance of meeting Carol on this occasion as she would probably be away with Harry.

These thoughts were passing through Forbes' mind as he drove into the steading. They were disturbing thoughts but he wouldn't allow them to become destructive. He had accepted that Carol Campbell was beyond his reach.

Crocuses

GAY little crocuses,
    Yellow and white,
Purple and lavender,
    Full of delight!

Gladness and joy are
    The gifts that you bring,
Chasing dark winter,
    Welcoming spring.

Bright little crocuses,
    Waking at dawn,
Smiling your message,
    That winter is gone.

Little birds twittering,
    They start to sing,
Sharing your gladness,
    That now it is spring.
— Patricia McGavock.

At the farm, he parked the car and got out. He was about to lift the rod from the passenger's seat when he stiffened and stood upright, listening. There was a noise.

The noise was repeated. It was a muffled shout, overlaid by loud bangings. It was coming from the direction of the steading. Forbes looked around hastily but there was no-one in sight.

He ran towards the building then realised that the noise was coming from the same loose box that had housed Silver, the stallion. The nearer

13

Forbes got, the louder the noise became. He climbed up on the half-door to the loose box and looked inside.

There he saw Carol Campbell cowering in a corner, her paints and canvasses strewn about the floor. Her face was ashen and her hands were covering her eyes.

She was half-moaning, half-shouting, "Help! Oh, help me, please help me."

Facing her, nostrils flared, ears flat and eyes gleaming wickedly, the stallion pawed the ground with an irregular beat of iron shoe against straw-covered cement.

Forbes summed up the position in a glance. He spoke quietly but firmly.

"Carol, it's all right. I'm here, Forbes Malcolm. Just do as I tell you and you won't get hurt."

Carol's hands dropped from her face and she stopped shouting. She gazed towards Forbes with fear imprinted on her face. Again Forbes spoke in the same level, authoratative tone.

"There is nothing to be afraid of, Carol. Just obey my instructions and you'll soon be out of there."

In the meantime, Forbes' voice had distracted Silver, but the stallion was still between Carol and the loose box door. The horse had ceased to paw the ground and his ears had pricked up. Forbes began his instructions.

Gradually, the girl moved along the wall until she was standing in the corner of the box next to Forbes. The horse backed off, uncertain about what was happening. With a crunching sound he stood heavily on Carol's paints and pulverised them.

"I'm going to open the door just a little," Forbes told the girl. "It will be open wide enough for you to squeeze through but we want to keep the horse on the opposite side of the door all the time. Wait until I give you the word."

Forbes bent down and grasped a handful of straw that had strayed beyond the door of the box. He held this in his left hand and offered it to the horse, trying to entice the stallion's head away from the door.

For a moment or two Silver gazed disdainfully at the straw, then curiosity won through and he took two steps towards Forbes' hand.

Almost simultaneously, Forbes slid back the bolt on the door with his right hand, pressed his weight against the door to open it a little.

"Right, Carol, now!" Forbes said urgently, and the girl squeezed out.

Forbes slammed the door shut and slid the bolt home with a great clang which made Silver bray and jump nervously.

CAROL clung to Forbes, sobbing and sobbing. He held her close and stroked her hair until she became calmer and quieter.

"Come on, let's go and sit in the car," he suggested, and led her gently across to sit in the passenger's seat.

She lay back, eyes closed, exhausted. Gradually, the colour came back to her cheeks and eventually she opened her eyes and looked at Forbes.

"How can I thank you?" she murmured. "That horse was going to trample me to death if you hadn't come along."

"Well, he certainly wasn't being very friendly, that's true." Forbes dared to smooth her hair from her forehead and he kissed a little frown that was puckering her brow.

She rested her head against his shoulder.

To distract her, Forbes asked, "What were you doing in that loose box anyway? I thought Harry was away today."

"Harry is away but I thought I'd get really close to Silver because I wanted to fill in some of the detail of colour in my painting. I didn't think there would be any danger."

She sat up. "Harry has gone over to Stirling to see his girlfriend, Evelyn. It's her birthday tomorrow and there's going to be a big party. I wouldn't be surprised if they announced their engagement then."

Forbes gazed incredulously at Carol.

"You mean you aren't Harry's girlfriend?" He stammered.

"*Me?*" It was Carol's turn to be amazed. "Certainly not! We've always been good friends and Harry has helped me a lot and is very interested in my work but I'm his cousin."

For a moment Carol looked at Forbes with a puzzled expression on her face, then she realised what had been in Forbes' mind.

She laughed.

"What a good thing this all happened, Forbes, because otherwise we'd never have met properly. First of all there was the business at the game fair . . . how angry you were." Her eyes teased him. "And then all your assumptions about me and Harry." She took Forbes' hand. "We are a pair, aren't we?"

"Never mind," Forbes said happily, "we can change all that now. And what about making a start by going into Inveraber now and replacing all your painting material? I don't suppose you want to give up painting Silver . . . he's too good a subject . . . and in any case I'm here to protect you from now on."

He switched on the car engine then turned to her again.

"You can give Harry the finished portrait as a wedding present!" □

The Gift
Of Happiness

IT had been coming to the hospital for over forty years now . . . that plain white envelope addressed in block letters, and containing only one small slip of paper and a bank note.
On the paper were just two words — *With Gratitude*.
At first the note had been a five pound one. Then it had been for ten

pounds, increasing in value at irregular intervals over the years until the last .few times a hundred pound note had come. No-one had ever discovered who sent it, nor had known what particular service rendered by the hospital was remembered in this way for so long, and always on the same day.

At the beginning not much attention had been paid. Then came a small fire in the hospital in which the only real loss was a number of records. So later on it was impossible to check which patients had been treated during the time leading up to the arrival of the first gift.

No-one seemed to recall anything beyond the usual routine of patients coming and going, and soon with changes in staff and the passing of years there seemed no likelihood of ever finding out.

It was all a great mystery.

Then at length the day came along when no envelope arrived in the post. Matron had been long enough in the hospital to have noted the date, and she looked through the mail that day with a feeling of real disappointment.

"I suppose we'll never know who was the generous friend." She sighed to Sister Rosemary Graham that evening. "Probably he or she has died, perhaps even in this very hospital. Imagine it! For forty years that gift has arrived on the same day without fail. But not today."

"It might just be delayed in the post," the Sister suggested.

Rosemary Graham had worked in this hospital for six years. In her late thirties now, she was a splendid nurse in every way, and perhaps the long spell in her earlier life when she cared for elderly parents had given her a special understanding of the needs of older patients who came in for treatment.

by ANNE MURRAY

Leaving Matron's office a few minutes later, she decided to return to Ward Three, just to make sure that old Mrs Bryant wasn't getting out of bed yet again, when she had been specially told not to do so.

Visiting hour for the evening had ended, and the long corridor was deserted, Rosemary walked lightly along, then halfway to the ward she stopped short. Something lay on the small table beside one of the windows, where a tasteful arrangement of flowers was always placed.

It wasn't the flowers she looked at. It was something beside the vase which hadn't been there when she passed along twenty minutes ago. It was a plain, white envelope, addressed to the hospital in block letters.

HURRYING back to Matron with the envelope, Rosemary's eyes were bright with interest.

"We were wrong, Matron!" she exclaimed. "The letter is here. I'm sure this is it. Don't you think so?"

"I do indeed!" Matron said excitedly as she tore open the envelope.

Yes, there it was. A hundred pound note, a slip of paper, and written on it were the words *With Gratitude*. But this time there was no stamp on the envelope. Someone had *placed* it on that table — someone who had actually been in the hospital a short time ago.

But who? A patient or a visitor? That was the question.

"We'll find out now," Matron decided confidently. "My guess is that our kind friend is a patient and one of her visitors put it where you found it. I'm certain it's a woman who remembers the date so faithfully. I can't think of it being a man!"

"Whoever it is must be elderly," Rosemary said. "Even someone of thirty when it all began would be seventy now."

"Have a good look round Ward Three and see if you think any of the ladies there fit the bill," Matron ordered. "I leave it to you."

Rosemary was just as anxious to solve the mystery. She returned to the ward and first of all glanced through the details of the patients there at the moment. Strangely enough, there weren't as many old ones as usual. Only three of them were over seventy.

It wasn't Mrs Bryant, she quickly decided. She was much too muddled over everything to do that sort of thing. Miss Ainsworth didn't seem to fit the bill either, with her constant criticism of everything and everybody. Mrs Elliot was eighty-six and far too frail to be bothering about gifts arriving on the right day.

It might be Mrs Manson? She seemed the type, but — no, forty years ago she would only be sixteen. No-one else seemed the least likely.

Rosemary sighed. The clue to the mystery didn't seem any nearer. For one thing, there was nothing to hinder someone walking into the hospital at visiting time, selecting a time when no-one was in the corridor, then laying down the enevelope.

Strangers were always coming and going at visiting hours. She decided to stop thinking about it and go round the ward for a brief chat with anyone who seemed to want a word.

Mrs Bryant had the usual grumble about the daughter-in-law who had visited her, and had brought in a bottle of orange juice.

Miss Ainsworth's complaint was that no-one at all had come to see her.

"Make the most of being young," she said severely to Rosemary. "When you're old and dull no-one wants to know you, not even for a five-minute visit."

Rosemary might have pointed out that perhaps it was this old lady's persistent grumbling and disapproval which kept away the friends who did come at times.

She passed on to Mrs Elliot, who was beckoning to her with a feeble wave of her hand. It seemed she had a bit of news to give Sister.

"I had a lovely surprise today,' she began. "My son walked in. He's in the Navy, you know, and has been away with his ship for two years. I didn't know he was due back so soon. It was wonderful to see him, for I really thought he might not be in time."

Rosemary couldn't protest that there was plenty of time. She knew this frail patient hadn't much left, but it was good that she was still so alert and that her son had come home to brighten her last days.

"But that's splendid," she said to Mrs Elliot. "I did notice that you had a handsome young man as your visitor this evening."

Mrs Elliot beamed happily.

"Yes, the nurses were all making eyes at him," she said with motherly pride. "You must come and speak to him tomorrow, Sister."

"Yes, of course." Rosemary smiled.

She realised later that the nurses were chattering to each other about Commander Elliot's appearance in the ward. All had been impressed by his good looks, and some had received the nicest of smiles.

"He's still a bachelor," young Nurse Evans announced. "Fancy that!"

"If his mother's eighty-six he must be older than he looks," decided Nurse Fraser, who hadn't been handy for one of the smiles and was feeling annoyed.

IT was the next evening when Rosemary saw Hugh Elliot come into the ward again. Tall and dark, he was certainly good looking and his eyes were the deep blue of the sea on a fine day, just right for a sailor.

When she was introduced to him she, too, thought he had a delightful smile.

"This is my son," old Mrs Elliot said, her voice seeming to have gained new strength as she looked up fondly at the young man.

It was across her bed that he shook hands with Rosemary, and when she moved on again after a few minutes chat she found herself approving of him quite a lot. Then when the visiting hour ended a message came to her that Mrs Elliot's visitor would like a word with her.

He was waiting just outside the ward door looking serious.

"I can see my mother isn't too good," he began. "Can anything be done?"

Rosemary's grey eyes were full of sympathy.

"I'm afraid not," she said gently. "It's just old age. But how good that you were able to come."

He nodded. "I'll come as often as I can as I suppose it may not be for long."

"I don't think so," Rosemary confirmed. "Yet your arrival has given her new strength."

"See you tomorrow, then," he told her. "Thanks, Sister, for all you're doing. I understand that you're the nicest person around!"

It was two days later that she found herself having quite a long chat with Mrs Elliot and her son. They didn't discuss illness at all, but a book the old lady had been reading whenever she felt up to it — a mystery story.

"My mother likes mystery stories," Hugh Elliot told Rosemary gravely. "But I'll bet she has already looked at the end of this book to see what happened."

"What nonsense!" Mrs Elliot exclaimed.

"Did you ever hear of the great hospital mystery?" Rosemary smiled.

"The anonymous gift?" Mrs Elliot queried. "Yes, I heard about it."

"The mystery has deepened," Rosemary went on. "This year it didn't come by post, but was found on a table in the corridor."

"So that was what it was," Hugh Elliot began, only to be abruptly silenced by a feeble smack on his hand from his mother.

"Will you be quiet?" she cried. "Talk about women letting out secrets! Men are far worse!"

Rosemary gazed at her in astonishment.

Was it possible? Had this frail old lady really been the one to send that gift, and had she been forced this year to ask her son to put the envelope in a conspicuous place? No, not that, for now she was reproving him.

"Hugh, I told you to post that letter."

"But why? I couldn't help seeing the address," he told her. "I'd have had to find a post office to get a stamp for one thing."

Mrs Elliot sank back on her pillows. "I still don't want anyone to know, not so long as I'm here," she whispered.

Amy

NO-ONE calls me by my first name any more.
　Who is there left who can be that familiar?
Mostly, I'm called Mum or Gran and, now, Great-Granny
And neighbours, not quite intimate, say "Mrs Kerr."
The nurse will gently bully in an efficient way.
Milkman, doctor and homehelp call me Mrs K.
Old friends are gone, and my precious younger brother,
Contemporary loved ones, husband, father, mother.
So who is there left to call me by my name?
Respectful youngsters dare not thus address me.
Oh, now, just once to hear an old beloved voice,
In sweet affection or chiding, say; "Amy."

— *Marion Jones.*

Rosemary took her hand. "I won't tell anyone," she promised. "Not even Matron."

Then she looked at Hugh Elliot. "Be sure you don't say any more," she warned him.

"I wouldn't dare say another word," he replied, with his irrepressible grin.

IT was later that evening, when the ward was quiet, that Rosemary heard the whole story from Mrs Elliot.

"You can tell anyone after I'm gone," she started off. "You see, I was over forty when I got married. Then I was expecting a baby, but I wasn't too well so I was brought in here about six weeks before the baby was due. My husband came in every day until — until one evening on his way to see me he was killed in a road crash."

"Oh, Mrs Elliot, how dreadful for you!" Rosemary exclaimed.

"The baby was born far too soon and there was something wrong with his heart. I was told he couldn't live without an operation, and even with one there was only a twenty per cent. chance of survival. I longed for him so, and I agreed to the operation. A clever surgeon came from somewhere and Baby got through the operation."

Had that tall strong man really begun life as a desperately ill baby, wondered Rosemary? She listened eagerly as Mrs Elliot went on.

"For two weeks his life hung in the balance. Every time a nurse came into the ward where I still lay quite ill, I thought this was it, he had gone. But suddenly, almost overnight, he took a turn for the better, gaining strength steadily until he was sturdy as they come.

"Caring for him helped me so much to get through the sad year after the death of my husband. At the end of that year I wanted to help the hospital in some way, to show my gratitude for all they had done."

"So you started sending the gift," Rosemary murmured.

"I couldn't spare much at first," the old lady told her. But year after year I made sure there was something to show I had never forgotten what had happened. If I hadn't had to come in here just now, no-one would ever have found out."

"And how wonderful for you to have such a strong healthy son," Rosemary said.

Mrs Elliot's eyes were closing.

"He likes you," she said drowsily. "He knows you haven't let out my secret . . . to please me . . ."

★   ★   ★   ★

It was a week later that she passed away quietly, and it was another ten days after that when Rosemary had a conversation with Commander Elliot before he went off again to rejoin his ship.

They stood in the corridor near the table on which that last gift had been placed, and he told her his mother's will contained a good legacy to the hospital.

"I'll be away only two or three months this time," he continued. "Will you write to me sometimes? I love my job, but in some ways it can be a lonely one. You can be lonely even with people all round you."

"I've discovered that, too," Rosemary said. "Yes, I'll be pleased to write you now and then. Will you write back?"

"Of course I will," he assured her.

It has to be admitted, however, that when Rosemary at last revealed the secret of the gift to Matron, that good lady received the news with mixed feelings.

"You mean you've known for weeks?" she exclaimed. "Sister, did I not ask you to tell me if you found out who was the sender?"

"But Mrs Elliot asked me not to tell until she was gone," Rosemary answered. "It was something her son said which revealed it was he who had put the envelope on the table."

Matron looked at her. Now why was this capable efficient Sister blushing like that? Oh dear, thought Matron. She also had met the good-looking Naval officer and had appreciated his charm.

Had something begun between these two? It seemed like it. To herself she gave a small resigned sigh. How tiresome it was when a first-rate Sister had to be replaced if she left to get married . . . □

Wher

by
KATE
MORTIMER

Tomorrow Comes

IT was during breakfast, that Thursday morning, when Sally decided, after another sleepless night, the time had come when she had got to act, to do *something*.

She just had to find out what was tearing Richard to pieces, underneath all that forced, brittle cheerfulness.

Watching him now, reading the letter from her brother and sister on holiday in Spain, she realised he wasn't taking in a word of it. Such a darling he was, she thought wryly. But he was no actor!

For the umpteenth time she wondered whether, deep down, he didn't really want the baby — or didn't feel that they were quite ready yet to start a family?

Or was she — in one of those strange moods which everyone said come to morning-sickness sufferers — just "imagining things"?

Her worst fear though, was that Richard could be ill, and trying to hide the fact. He worked so hard, and if he was sapping his strength and energy, that could make him pale and tense.

One thing she was sure about now — it wasn't simply that all he was thinking about was dreaming up new designs.

Sally had learned right from their beginning, that those who work creatively with wood are artists — just like those who work with words, or music, or paint.

Sometimes they had to retreat into another world, as Richard had done. And she had learned to wait, and not fuss, until he was ready to tell her all about it, as he always did.

But even so, she had to admit this was something quite different.

Now, as he put the letter down and started on his last cup of coffee, Sally said, "They seem to be having a whale of a time, don't they?".

"Yes," he said, but his eyes were glazed and far away. He put the cup on the table and stood up.

"Well, must dash now." He kissed her lightly. "Now just because you are feeling better don't go rushing about trying to do too much."

"I won't," Sally said. "But Richard . . ."

At the kitchen door, he turned back.

"I . . . you . . . will you do something for me? Something special."

"Of course. Anything," he said promptly.

"Will you take me to lunch today, at the Burrell Gallery in Pollok Park?"

Sally saw first astonishment, then unmistakably, a flicker of irritation in his eyes.

But he managed a laugh.

"Is this one of those sudden ideas pregnant women are given to?"

"Not exactly." Sally smiled, too, but inside a small voice was saying *now or never.* "I want to go there today, for . . . for a very

23

special . . . purpose. And a very important one, too. I know you are terribly busy just now, but . . ."

"To do with the baby?"

Sally hesitated, and then she thought, well wasn't it, ultimately, to do with the baby, to do with the three of them?

"Yes, love," she said. "It is."

Richard turned away to open the door, but when he looked back he was smiling.

"OK," he said, "I'll humour you. Be ready about eleven-thirty and I'll collect you."

SALLY watched him disappear down the road of small terraced houses in their little old banger.

"It's worth a try," she said aloud then, vehemently, "more than a try. It's *got* to work. It's just got to."

Systematically she went through her morning chores, doing the dishes, tidying their bedroom and vacuuming the carpet in the living-room. Then she changed into her new smock, and comfortable shoes, before going back down to the kitchen to wait.

As so often, Sally stood in front of the framed newspaper cutting on the kitchen wall — ever her inspiration and joy.

It didn't seem possible that it was three years now since she had seen the advertisement.

Girl Friday wanted, with initiative, energy, shorthand typing and humour — to help in new business.

Splendid prospects for wood and tree lover willing to dogsbody at first. But promotional halo will come.

Apply Richard Sinclair, 55a Garrett Street.

It was so crazy, Sally had been drawn to it immediately. Especially as she'd just had to leave a difficult job working for one of those married men with a roving eye.

She could still remember how her antennae tingled when she'd first seen the big shed Richard was converting behind his father's garage business.

A long, gangling body was draped around a very dodgy-looking drainpipe. The flushed cheeks were decorated with a ginger beard, and the head topped by a tousled crop of thick ginger hair.

"Hello," he'd said blithely, waving a black paint brush. "Sinclair's Shambles, being transformed into Sinclair's Shangri-la."

"I see. I've come about your advertisement," Sally had replied.

And at that he'd shinned down the drainpipe at the speed of light.

"I've done some dogsbodying to earn the money for my secretarial course," she'd added. "I want something . . . different."

"Hm." Richard had grinned impishly. "You'll get that here all right. I earned the money to start this place by working on an oil rig!"

He'd put down the brush and paint tin and led her inside — a wonderful shambles of wood and sawdust, of finsished and unfinished furniture, and sculptures in wood of birds, animals and bowls.

Sally had sniffed the air.

"What a gorgeous smell," she'd breathed, "of pine . . . and everything!"

Richard had beamed at her and then shouted to the wonderful old man with sparkling blue eyes and long flowing white hair.

"Hear that, Ben. We've got a treasure!"

Dear Ben had put down the grandfather clock he was working on, and Richard told her he'd taught him everything he knew about wood at the local Technical School.

"He's a genius."

Ben had just smiled. "I've come out of mothballs to lend a hand and keep an eye on him!"

WHAT joyous days they were, Sally thought now, just the three of them. But even then the quality of the workmanship was recognised, as well as Richard's enterprise and enthusiasm.

Customers didn't only come to admire. They came to buy — and they told their friends.

▶ *over*

according to Custom

EVERY November thousands of Londoners turn out to see the newly-elected Lord Mayor parade through the city streets. It's a tradition that goes back some seven hundred years when King John declared that the new Lord Mayor must publicly present himself to his citizens. The Mayor travels in a magnificent gilded coach with his attendants in a procession that ranks alongside the great State occasions.

And for several months, she had swept up the shavings, washed the floors, and answered the telephone, as well as sorting out the paper work — for Richard's way with paper was far from being as skilled as his way with the wood from which it was made!

It was after they'd taken on an extra girl to handle the telephone, and two more of Ben's former students from the Technical School that Richard had said abruptly:

"You realise now that you've really become part of the furniture?"

"You mean good solid wood?" she queried.

"I told Ben that first day you were the girl for me . . . and I've hoped ever since that . . ." he stopped.

"Would this be a proposal, Mr Sinclair?" she teased. "Because if so, I think you could improve on the wording."

And he had done, with speed and love.

Oh, that wonderful understanding growing stronger and stronger between them. Even her parents, initially a bit uncertain because of their roots in security, had come round in the end.

But I couldn't have talked to them about this, Sally told herself now, nor Richard's parents. It would be disloyal. Only I . . .

The toot of the horn outside jerked her out of her reverie.

I WANT to call somewhere to . . . to get something, before we go to Pollok Park," she told Richard as she fastened her seat belt.

"Really. You're very mysterious," he said.

"I know. But you'll see why and I think you'll . . . be pleased," she told him. "Only don't ask any questions 'cos you've got to wait and see.

"I've just been looking at our advertisement, remembering those days," she said, as they started the twenty minutes or so drive into Glasgow. "Beginnings are so wonderful."

"Yes," Richard said, "But . . ." Then his voice tailed away.

Sally didn't ask him to explain that "but." She knew she had to bide her time. The moment would come.

It was only when they had driven into the city, that she spoke again. "I want you to park down that next street on the left and wait." She kissed him lightly. "And don't you dare try to follow me!"

"No, ma'am," he said, and just for an instance Sally saw a glimpse of the old schoolboy grin so typical of him.

She turned back out of the side street and went into the craft shop just round the corner, where she had come a few weeks ago to order her wedding anniversary present for Richard.

"Of course, we'll hold it for you, Mrs Sinclair," the assistant had said. "Just let us know when, and what time you'd like us to deliver."

And now they were equally accommodating.

"Of course I'll carry it round to your car," the assistant said, after Sally had explained that she had a very special reason for wanting her husband to have it now.

"Well," Richard said after he'd carefully put it in the boot of the car,

"I suppose it's no use my asking whether that's a box of lead?"

"Not a bit of use. Wait and see," Sally told him. "Pollok Park now, please, driver! And thank goodness the sun is shining and the grass is dry."

"You're enjoying yourself enormously, aren't you?"

"Well, I wasn't . . . but I am now . . . well almost." And I am, Sally thought, but I'm scared, too, because if this fails, what in the world can I do next!

In Pollok Park he glanced across at her.

"Are we taking your load of lead into the Galleries?"

"We are not. Please drive down here and stop beside *our* tree . . . that's right. Now, you can get out, and remove the wrapping from the parcel . . . that's right, lean it up against this Scots pine . . ."

Sally flopped back on her haunches and watched him, her heart in her mouth as, finally, he reached the slim square cardboard box and opened it.

H IS gasp of sheer joy and awe, as he took out the picture, lifted her heart. He leaned it against the tree, then came back and flopped down beside her, holding her tightly.

Together they gazed at that wide, winding river, flanked by mountains and forests, with little red log cabins dotting the lower slopes.

"Those logs . . . that bridge . . . it . . ."

"It's almost our bridge, isn't it?" Sally breathed. "As soon as I saw it, I knew you'd love it, too.

"Oh, Richard, do you remember what you said . . . that those logs floating down the river are living . . . that some crash along so full of verve. Others come slowly, are more dignified . . ."

"Oh, of course I remember," he said, and the strain had gone from his voice. "And we laughed about those logs which just slip themselves into a tiny inlet and stay there, stuck quite happily like people who don't want adventure.

"Oh, Sally, it's the most wonderful present . . . for our anniversary? Our wonderful honeymoon . . . dear, dear Norway!"

He hugged her ecstatically. And then Sally said very quietly but very firmly, "It's your anniversary gift from me, yes. But there's a condition."

Richard just laughed.

"OK, I'll fulfil it."

"You'd better. Do you remember on that bridge, we also said we'd never have any secrets from each other. We'd never hide even our little fears from each other.

"Sometimes you might go into your shell to work on ideas, but we'd share everything." She hesitated and then added deliberately, "*Everything.*"

"As we have," he said quickly.

"Until the last few weeks, yes," Sally said. Then, taking his hands, she asked him, "Richard, are you really and truly happy about the baby . . ?"

His genuine astonishment was all the answer she needed for that one. "Of course I am. How can you doubt it?"

"Well, it's just that at times . . ."

"Oh, I see what you mean. I fuss you and worry about you. That's right." He laughed. "I even went to see Dr King about you last week, and he said expectant fathers always suffer terribly with their first! So stop worrying, I'm thrilled so long as you don't do silly things, or worry yourself. Now, what about lunch?"

"Not yet," Sally said. Then she sat up straight. "So, if you're happy about the baby, if you are OK, what's going on? What are you fighting? Or who? Because these last weeks I'm sure there is something tearing you to pieces . . . and that this time it is *not* just creative dreaming. Looks to me more like some nightmare you're hiding from me.

"Richard, stop trying to laugh it off. Stop pretending. I thought . . . hoped . . . that here, beneath 'our' tree where we got engaged . . . that with this reminder of our honeymoon in Norway . . ." her voice broke . . . "Until now, the man I married always trusted me with the truth."

The Rainbow

STORM clouds hung low as thunder
rolled,
And soon the rain fell fast.
Lightning flashed and people splashed
Through puddles as they passed.
Bedraggled cats sought sheltered nooks,
Umbrellas hurried by,
With huddled souls beneath them
Intent on keeping dry.
The unprepared soaked to the skin
To destinations rushed.
It seemed the rain would fall all day
As down the drains it gushed.
And then the clouds began to lift
And soon the sun shone through.
Then, shining in the Heavens,
A bow of every hue!
We never need to feel depressed
Or let our spirits wane;
For God has made a promise
And the sun shines through the rain.
— *Beatrice Huntingdon.*

HE reacted sharply to that.

"My dear, dear Sally, you know I've never lied to you, and I never would."

"Of course you haven't. But you have . . . sort of by omission — by hiding something. Either it's illness . . ."

He looked earnestly into her eyes and gripped her hands.

"I . . . I'm a bit worried, but truly it has nothing to do with my health. I'm fine. It's just that . . . that . . . well, I didn't want to worry you with it now . . . nor Ben, cos he's in a lot of pain, while waiting for his operation. I couldn't bother Dad and Mum, they've got problems enough of their own and . . ."

"Stop thinking aloud, and tell *me* now . . ." Sally pleaded.

"It's . . . well, it's the Salters account. You know how big they are, and what a lot of stuff they've bought. It's the biggest we ever had and I didn't want to fuss for payment, so I let it run on and on. But . . . well, it seems he isn't so safe and solid as we thought and . . . and that he's a bit of a gambler . . ."

For a few moments Sally said nothing. But then she asked him, "I can see it knocks us back only . . . only it couldn't break us, could it?"

"Not quite. Only . . . what's really been on my mind, love, is that I've had a very good offer from a big company in London . . ."

"Oh, no. You can't give up and go to London, not after all we've worked for and achieved?" Sally cried.

"Go to London? Me?" Richard laughed. "Not on your nelly! No, this firm wants to *buy* Sinclairs, but to leave me in control . . . listen and don't say anything yet . . . It would mean security for us, more money, we could move to a bigger house with a bigger garden. I could give you things I want to . . ."

"Stop!" Sally cried. "Can we pull through without . . . without this?"

"Yes, we *could*. We're sound, and we've good customers. Salters say that they'll pay . . . eventually."

Sally hugged him tightly.

"My dear love," she cried, "I don't want a bigger house. I love our little one and the small garden, our very first home. And we both love Sinclairs as much as the baby we're going to have. It is *our* baby, and we can't sell it, not for all the money in the world."

Sally pulled his arms and they stood up, facing the picture.

"I'll tell you something," she said with a happy, relieved laugh. "I've been dreaming up such horrors that could be wrong that this, awful though it is, seems almost trivial by comparision. Richard, this morning I asked you if you'd do something for me, if you'd bring me here."

"And I said, yes of course!"

"Right. You said you'd do anything for me. So . . ." She laughed outright. "Will you put the picture back in the car? Will you take me to that wonderful restaurant with the woodwork you admire so much, in the house? And then . . . ?

"Then, when we've eaten, will you please drive us home and telephone that firm in London and tell them absolutely firmly and definitely that you've decided not to sell Sinclairs?"

He put a hand on top of her head, and stroked her hair, as if in a blessing, and his voice was not quite steady when he said quietly, "Will do."

"And there's another thing," Sally went on, as they started to walk to the house after stowing the picture. "Now I'm through the worst of morning sickness, I can come back to the office again for a little while at least."

"Will *not* do!" Richard said.

"Will see . . . !"

They went into the house, laughing. □

by PHYLLIS HEATH

On Mother's Special Day

S HEILA opened her eyes as she heard the bedroom door click.
"I'm awake," she called sleepily as her daughter peeped round.

"Well, almost. And I certainly will be when I've drunk some of that coffee. Haven't you brought yourself one?" she asked, levering herself upright.

"Of course!" Julie disappeared to come back inside a moment later, carrying a second cup and holding an envelope in her free hand. "There!" she said, propping the envelope against her mother's cup.

"Happy Mother's Day . . . next . . ."

"But that's next week, isn't it? I haven't got the date wrong, have I?"

"No, Mother. If you'd just let me finish, that was what I was going to say. Happy Mother's Day, next week. It's just that . . . well, open the envelope and then you'll understand."

Sheila picked up the envelope, weighing it speculatively in her hand.

She forced a finger under the flap and tore open the envelope. Colourful flowers and a warm greeting in gilt, confirmed what Julie had said. Sheila raised her eye enquiringly as she opened the card to read the signature, and as she opened it a thin slip of blue paper fluttered down on to the coverlet.

Again her glance went to Julie as she picked it up.

"It's a ticket! A ticket to Alan Baker's concert! Isn't he . . . ?"

"Yes, Mother! Of course he is! One of the Big Bands, like Joe Loss and Glenn Miller, that you're always talking about."

Sheila caught the slightly-irritable note in her daughter's voice and quickly checked the date on the ticket.

"Oh, Saturday! Lovely! I haven't a thing on. What a lovely idea, darling."

"I thought you'd like it. Well, it was Bob's idea, really. And you'd better have something on," she said, her eyes gleaming with mischief. "Something very special, if Bob and I are taking you out."

"You and Bob? You've got tickets, too?"

"Of course! You don't think we'd let you go on your own, do you? Besides," Julie hurried on. It was over eighteen months since her father had died, but she guessed the music of her youth might rouse some sad memories for her mother.

"Bob rather likes that sort of music. Of course, he's rather old fashioned, too."

"Watch it!" Sheila warned, glad of a way to mask her feelings.

Though she and Tom had met during the big band era, Tom hadn't enjoyed dancing very much, and, as their friendship had grown, they had gone less and less to the local dance halls. It had been one of the minuses of their courtship and eventual marriage. Though there had been many, many pluses to compensate, Sheila reminded herself, with that tightening round her heart that still came with the memories of her husband.

But, of course, Julie hadn't known of this. All she had heard was her mother's talk of the melodies of her younger days, and the musicians which, in her eyes and ears, far out-did the modern pop groups. And, as she also knew, Sheila had met Tom at the Palais.

She probably hadn't recalled Sheila's teasing remarks about Tom's two left feet.

WE did have fun," Sheila mused now, sipping her coffee. "There were a crowd of us — all girls. We used to go every Saturday night to one dance or another. Then you got asked to dance, properly, none of this, 'Are you dancing,' stuff. We'd have soon dealt with any boy who didn't ask nicely."

She grinned at her daughter's expression.

"Oh, you can laugh. But people were different then, I'm sure."

"Did you have lots of partners? I bet you did."

"Flattery will get you anywhere. But, yes, I suppose I did. But, there were lots of boys . . ."

"And you met Dad there . . . Mum?" Julie's voice was hesitant. "Bob said you'd enjoy going, but . . . it won't be too sad, will it? You're not upset that we got the tickets?"

"Of course not! You know how I wallow in the old films, and I saw most of them with your dad. Don't worry, love. It's a marvellous Mother's Day present. You hold on tight to your Bob, he's a caring sort of person."

"I know." Julie hugged her mother, then turned to pick up the coffee cups. "I wish Dad could have been here for my wedding."

"We'll miss him, of course, but . . . he wouldn't have wanted us to go on being unhappy, Julie. That way, I think, would spoil the years we did have."

"I suppose so. Yes, I agree. Dad would want you to be happy."

Sheila echoed this sentiment as she prepared for her evening out with Julie and her fiancé, humming some of the remembered tunes as she applied her make-up.

THOUGH Tom hadn't enjoyed dancing much himself, he had been willing to take Sheila along, and for several months they had joined the crowd of friends in which they'd met. But, gradually, other pairs had been formed, outside as well as inside the group, so it had been easier to find the sort of entertainment they could enjoy together.

Yes, Sheila thought, spraying perfume behind her ears, tonight held its measure of sentiment for the youthful days, and maybe the dawning of her love for Tom. Nostalgia was probably a better word for what she would experience tonight.

As will plenty more people, she smiled, as the three of them joined the crowds streaming into the concert hall. Except for a sprinkling of young people the majority of the audience were grey haired, or nearly so, and Sheila spotted many couples she knew.

Settling in her seat she glanced along the rows, watching as heads turned, everyone like herself seemingly searching the faces of those around them.

It was strange to look into features, blurred with the years and memory, and sometimes recognise a face from her youth. To smile, hesitantly, unsure if her guess was correct, and if she had been recognised in return.

As the first foot-tapping notes hit the air Sheila relaxed, the familiar words flooding into her mind, the musicians and their gleaming instruments carrying her back down the years. The haunting melodies of the war years, the crescendos of numbers like *American Patrol*, the beat of, *In The Mood*, transporting the audience to another time and place.

When thunderous applause announced the interval, Sheila followed Bob and Julie out into the corridors in a daze.

"I'll get some drinks," Bob suggested. "What would you like, Mrs Holcombe?"

"Coffee, please. I think I'm already slightly tipsy." Sheila laughed.

"Then I'll get the coffee, Bob. Don't go away," Julie warned her mother as the two of them hurried off.

Sheila strolled around the small reception hall. In one corner several young women were selling records and she watched, catching sight of the faces of musicians and singers she knew, on the record sleeves.

Various people came in carrying glasses and cups but there was no sign of her daughter. She wandered over to where some photos of the members of the band were displayed. One, a man in his late fifties, carried the caption that he had played in this very town.

Squinting through half-closed eyes Sheila tried to identify the man, imagining a little more hair and a slightly less rotund figure. But, though she could remember the band, and the dance hall they'd played in, she couldn't recall this particular musician. She shrugged as she passed on to the next picture.

I SUPPOSE we all get older," A voice spoke almost in her ear, bringing Sheila spinning round.

The man who was standing close behind her took a hurried step backwards, his face flushing.

"I'm sorry, I didn't mean . . . Of course that remark doesn't include you ladies," he ended, recovering as she smiled at him.

"A for effort. Isn't that what they used to say when we were at school? But I'm afraid it isn't the truth."

Sheila studied the man, as she had the picture, trying to wipe away the changes the years had brought in him.

"Don't I know you? Or, didn't I? Jerry? Jerry Jones! Of course!

"I'm sorry," she went on, hesitantly. "I thought . . .

"It's all right. Yes, I'm Jerry, Sheila. I just couldn't believe it was you."

Sheila pulled a face. "Like you say, we've all changed, unfortunately."

"No, no. You haven't . . . not much, anyway. And your voice . . . I knew I'd recognise that. Voices don't change. That's why I spoke."

"You mean . . . ?" Sheila wasn't sure she wanted to go into what this man from the past did mean. He was smiling at her with such frank approval that she felt the colour mounting to her cheeks.

"How's . . . your husband? Is he with you?" Jerry turned his head to survey the crowd around them. "Of course, I didn't know him very well."

"Tom died. Nearly two years ago, now."

"I'm sorry. I've been away, down south, I didn't know."

"But you still live in Brentford?"

"It's my base, I suppose, but I travel a lot. I did marry, but —" He shrugged. "It didn't work out. Luckily, in one way, we didn't have a family, so I've nothing to keep me here. But I made it tonight because of Les."

Sheila looked puzzled until Jerry pointed to the picture she'd been studying earlier.

"Of course! Les Wellington. I'd forgotten, you and he were friends."

"I don't make it to many of his concerts, but I try. I'm glad I made it tonight."

Sheila turned away, quickly searching the crowd for her daughter. Watching her, Jerry began to apologise.

"I'm sorry. I'm keeping you. You'll be with someone."

"No, well, yes, my daughter and her fiancé. Though I can't think what happened to the coffee Julie was supposed to be bringing me. Perhaps I ought to see if I can find them. Actually Julie told me to wait in the hallway."

She turned towards the door, realising that the crowd was thinning.

"There she is, and Bob. I'd better make my apologies. It's been nice . . ."

She didn't finish the sentence as Jerry took her arm, steering her in the direction of Julie.

"I can do that for you, tell them it was all my fault," he whispered, as they drew near.

Sheila laughed up at him, just as Julie caught sight of her.

"Mum?" the girl began and, true to his word, Jerry spoke.

"I'm sorry. Your mother and I are old friends. We've been catching up and quite forgot the time."

"Oh, I see. Well, your coffee's cold now, Mother. And the bell's gone. I think we ought to go back inside."

She slipped her hand under her mother's arm but Sheila held back.

"You go ahead. I won't be a moment, Julie. I must say goodbye to Jerry." Sheila turned to where Jerry was standing watching them. "There's a few minutes yet."

SHE walked back to Jerry, and after a shrug, Julie followed Bob through the doors.

"I'm sorry you didn't get your coffee," Jerry said. "Perhaps we could meet sometime — for a drink, or a meal."

"That would be nice."

Now that she had come back to him Sheila was beginning to wish she hadn't. Yet it had seemed only courteous not to leave Jerry so abruptly.

"I don't even know your name."

Sheila looked surprised then she laughed. "No, of course, you mean Tom's name. We sort of drifted away from the rest of you, once Tom and I . . .

according to Custom

IN olden times, it is said, butter and eggs were forbidden during Lent, so on Shrove Tuesday — the day before Ash Wednesday — housewives used up their stocks to make pancakes. Today Pancake Day is marked by many different events all over the country. At Olney in Buckinghamshire the annual race is held. It came about, it is believed, when a housewife, in the middle of her pancake making, was summoned to church by the bell calling all to absolution. She set off in haste, complete with frying pan and batter.

"Fell in love? You did, didn't you? It was one of those boy and girl affairs that worked out. It did, didn't it? I mean, you stayed together."

"We were happy, yes."

"I'm glad. And now you'll miss him."

"Yes. I don't suppose I'll ever stop, but . . . you have to adjust, have to take up your life again."

They had moved slowly away from the entrance to the concert hall and Jerry hesitated by a seat set in an alcove.

"They've started," he told her. "We'll have to wait until they finish this number. We might as well have a seat."

Briefly, Sheila hesitated but then, with a smile, she sat down. "We can hear them, we'll know when the tune ends."

She tilted her head, listening to the music. "It's rather like sitting on those couches they used to have over one side at the Palais, remember them?"

"Do I! I made all my best conquests there. The dim lighting, the smoochy music, not forgetting that touch of luxury, a glass of lemonade."

"Oh, Jerry! You were always fun."

"We had some good times, didn't we?"

As tune followed tune they sat, recalling those evenings, talking of first one of their old friends and then another, running backwards and forwards across the years.

It was the absolute thunderous applause and cheering which brought Sheila finally back to the present. She clapped a hand across her mouth in horror as she saw the doors being thrown open and the first of the audience emerging.

A Missed Summernight's Dream

MY head is in a turmoil,
My mind is on the boil,
I've had a day of toil,
But sleep won't come.

My partner rests tranquil,
He falls asleep at will,
I try to keep quite still,
But sleep won't come.

I think of pleasant things,
A rose and mannequins,
Of Callas when she sings,
But sleep won't come.

A kind and loving mother,
A tempestuous Latin lover,
A pretty patchwork cover,
But sleep won't come.

I try to count some sheep,
I've heard this will bring sleep,
Over a gate they leap,
But sleep won't come.

I breathe in long and deep,
I exercise my feet,
I rearrange the sheet,
But sleep won't come.

I glance towards the clock,
I hear its soft tick-tock,
It will ring at six o'clock,
Then sleep will come.

Anne Anderson.

36

On Mother's Special Day

"Oh, Jerry, the concert's over. We've sat talking here all through the second half."

"Well, don't look so worried. It isn't a punishable offence, is it?"

"Not exactly. But Julie and Bob brought me because it's Mother's Day tomorrow. Oh dear! That's brought me down to earth. My daughter is twenty-five!"

"So what! Look, Sheila, before this daughter of yours comes and whisks you away, you will see me again, won't you? Give me your phone number, please!"

"Well . . . Just for a drink, maybe, since I never got my coffee. Perhaps we could arrange a reunion, sort of? Ask some of the others?"

"We'll see! Your number, quick! Here's your daughter."

Sheila gabbled the number, getting to her feet as Julie drew near.

"I'm sorry, love. Jerry and I got talking and we didn't notice the time. I did enjoy the first half, it wasn't that . . . Though it did seem a bit louder than I remember our music used to be. Wouldn't you agree, Jerry?"

"Yes, loud enough to hear out here. In fact, I think I enjoyed it better from this distance.

"Thanks for lending me your mother for part of the evening," he told Julie. "I'll call you Sheila."

JULIE turned in her seat as they settled in Bob's car. "Have you really not met him since you were a girl, Mother?"

"No, but it really isn't that long . . . at least, it didn't seem so tonight."

"Did I hear him say he was going to phone you?"

"Oh, people say these things. I don't suppose he will. It's almost thirty years since we knew each other. Thirty years!"

Sheila sat back in her seat. Thirty years! Well, perhaps not quite so many. But she was getting old. She and Jerry were both old.

But it had been a lovely evening, she thought as she settled down to sleep. And tomorrow it is Mother's Day. Julie will spoil me, bringing breakfast in bed. And there'll be cards from Ian and Carol. Presents, too, I shouldn't be surprised. What more could I wish for?

The next day turned out just as she'd predicted, with the added bonus that her son and his wife came for a visit, bringing their small gifts.

Later, as she watched television, her eyes almost closing, the telephone rang. Julie came back from answering.

"It's for you, Mum. Jerry, he said. Wasn't that the man you met last night?" She smiled.

Sheila nodded, moving out into the hall to take the call.

She was gone several minutes and Julie was waiting, expectantly as she came back into the sitting-room.

"Well?" she asked.

"Now don't start jumping to conclusions. Jerry's an old friend. We're just meeting for a drink. That's all." Sheila bent to kiss her daughter. "Thanks for a lovely day. And for my present. It was the nicest Mother's Day gift you could have made me." □

37

by MARGARET BLACK

A GNES BENZIE did not like her new neighbours. Not that there was anything particularly remarkable in that. She hadn't been fond of some of her old neighbours, either.

But at least the old, draughty, inconvenient Glasgow tenement flat she had left had thick walls. This new, modern, bright and easily-heated one did not.

Her new neighbours through the wall appeared to spend the whole day with their radio going full blast, while the family upstairs tramped around in what Agnes Benzie referred to mentally as "tackety boots."

Her other neighbours, across the landing, had a young baby who cried a lot.

Agnes liked a quiet existence. She was a thin, upright woman of sixty-one and her nose and chin dominated her face.

She was not a handsome woman but that had long since ceased to worry her.

Once upon a time, in the dim and distant past, Sandy, her husband, had whispered in her ear, "Darling, you're beautiful!" and she had glowed with tenderness, not believing him but wanting to.

But Sandy was dead these fourteen years and, since then, the heart and soul of the woman's being had been centred on her son Michael, born when she was almost forty — a miracle, it had seemed to Sandy and herself.

Her pride in the rather quiet, clever little boy had been boundless. Michael had done exceptionally well at school and gone to Edinburgh to university.

That was when he changed. From the quiet boy, who conformed unprotestingly to his mother's expectations, he suddenly became a stranger. He rarely wore anything but jeans and cropped his curly hair so short that his mother complained he looked like a convict.

He stopped coming home every weekend to have his washing done and started going out with girls. He also stopped listening to advice, especially from his mother.

The woman had always looked forward to the time when Michael would bring home some nice, serious-minded girl.

He brought girls, all right, but they looked much like Michael himself, except for the length of their hair, and she didn't think they had a serious thought in their heads — talk of pop music and discos was all she ever heard.

Michael was three months past his twentieth birthday when he told his

THE FOLK NEXT DOOR

mother he wanted to get married. She was shocked and outraged.

"I haven't even met the girl! Who is she?"

"You have met her! She's Claire!"

The name meant nothing.

"I brought her at Christmas," he persisted. "You must remember her — blonde and tall. Mum, I love her —"

"You've got nothing to get married on," Agnes Benzie's voice shook. "No home — no money — no job —"

She knew by the blank look on her son's face that she wasn't getting through to him but she went on trying, for all it was like chipping at a boulder with a nail file.

IN spite of everything his mother could say, every argument she could dredge up, Michael and Claire were married.

Agnes wasn't even at the wedding and that hurt her deeply, even although it wasn't — in her eyes — a proper wedding at all, because Claire's parents were abroad.

"We're just going to the Registrar's with the witnesses, Mum. We don't want a fuss."

She hadn't been able to hide her feelings — and the resultant coldness had lasted. She and Claire had nothing in common and they never seemed to have anything to talk about. Visits became fewer and finally stopped, although Michael came occasionally and tried to make excuses.

"Claire's working in a shop at weekends. We need the money for the rent."

With an effort, Agnes managed to say nothing about marrying before he had a job but Michael saw the tightening of his mother's lips and his blue eyes, so like his father's, grew cold.

"Why don't you like Claire, Mum?" he'd demanded baldly that day.

"I don't dislike her. I don't *know* her — and I just think you should have waited, got yourself settled in life before you married." Agnes had tried to reason.

"You don't want to know her! She feels unwelcome when she comes here."

"That's a terrible thing to say —" she broke off, unable to believe they were quarrelling, her and Michael.

The quarrel didn't last but the coolness did and Claire never came over from Edinburgh.

So now, this autumn day, Agnes Benzie sat in her bright room with the dust motes spinning in the sunlight from the window, and not a sound in the flat but the unwelcome noises made by her new neighbours.

The baby was crying again, fretfully and persistently. It interrupted her concentration on the letter she was trying to write to her son.

She wrote dutifully every week and always found difficulty filling two sheets, because there was never anything real to say, and because she could not write from the fullness of her heart. So the letters were stilted and said nothing but she continued to write them out of a sense of duty — and because she was determined not to put herself in the wrong.

Michael wrote scrappy notes occasionally but Claire never wrote at all.

Presently the woman laid aside her unfinished letter. Being on her own rarely troubled her but today she felt strangely restless. Being uprooted from the familiar surroundings of Govan had unsettled her.

She missed Florrie Emslie, her old neighbour of nearly thirty years, who had moved away to live with her married daughter in East Kilbride.

It was a nice afternoon, so Agnes decided she would go out. She lengthened her time out of the house by going for a walk in the park, but it was still only an hour later that she faced her own door and found she had forgotten her key and locked herself out.

Blankly she stared at the bright, newly-painted door, remembering how she had left the key in her other handbag. Desperately she rattled the door handle, as if by some magic she could open it.

There was no-one on the stairs and a hush hung over the entry. For the first time since she had moved into the building, it seemed, there was peace and quiet — just when she didn't want it. Back in the old tenement she had always left a key with Florrie Emslie, in case of an emergency like this — an emergency which never happened.

AGNES BENZIE was still standing, feeling helpless, when a young man climbed the stairs behind her. He had red hair and a freckled face and he smiled and said hello, as he inserted his key in the door across the landing.

"I have," Agnes said uncertainly, feeling rather foolish, "locked myself out."

The young man swung round.

"Too bad. Would you like me to try my key?"

It wouldn't turn, although he twisted it until she was sure it would break in the lock.

"I'll get a joiner," she said hastily.

"Not very easy on a Saturday afternoon. If I had a ladder I might get in the back window. I'll go and get Johnnie Renfrew from upstairs. He should have a ladder in his van. He's a painter —"

In no time, it seemed to Agnes Benzie, she found herself swamped by a tide of her new and noisy neighbours.

Johnnie Renfrew was a middle-aged man, part of the family who tramped about so noisily upstairs, and it seemed that nearly all his

Echoes

SOMETIMES, when the evening star
  Twinkles brightly from afar,
And gentle moonlight's silvery calm
Enfolds one, like a friendly arm,
In the midnight hush I hear
Children's voices, shrill and clear,
Laughing, singing . . . and I know
They're echoes from so long ago!

And sometimes, at the dawn of day,
When the first light, chill and grey,
Steals across the eastern sky,
I lie, and think of days gone by.
Then, in the stillness, so it seems,
Those voices break into my dreams,
And though I know they're fully grown,
With homes and children of their own,
My little ones come back to me,
Just the way they used to be.

Down the corridor of years,
Invoking thoughts too deep for tears,
Those voices call . . . I hope that they
Will never, wholly, fade away . . .
— Kathleen O'Farrell.

41

family clattered down to help. The neighbours with the radio were an elderly couple, the man very lame and wearing a hearing aid — but vociferous with advice about how to get into the house.

"We've got the phone. I'll call the Fire Brigade."

"No!" Agnes Benzie protested, feeling everything was getting out of hand.

"Come in and sit down. Leave them to get on with it." The young woman with the baby put her hand firmly on Agnes Benzie's arm and led her into the house across the landing, pushing her gently into a seat.

"Could you hold the baby for a minute? He's driving me frantic."

Agnes held the squirming baby against her shoulder, patting his back gently with a practised hand. It was over twenty years since she had nursed a baby but some skills are never forgotten.

Over the baby's head she looked round the room. The furniture was too modern for her taste, but it was well polished and there were flowers on the sideboard.

The young woman returned with a steaming cup of tea and a plate of biscuits.

"I'm Jill Hunter," she said, relieving Agnes of her burden. "You must be Mrs Benzie. I saw your name on your door, so I know you're our new neighbour. This —" she indicated the baby, now mercifully dropping off to sleep with his thumb in his mouth "— is Peter."

Agnes accepted the tea and sipped it gratefully, refusing a biscuit.

"Does Peter disturb you, Mrs Benzie?" the girl went on. "He cries such a lot. The nurse says it's baby colic and he'll grow out of it."

"He doesn't bother me," the woman returned untruthfully, looking up at the girl's flushed face. She had nice brown eyes and a head of untidy dark hair.

"You'll have had a family of your own?" Jill Hunter rocked the baby gently.

"One son — he's married and lives in Edinburgh."

"Ron — that's my husband — he's an only son, too. I wish he wasn't."

Labour Of Love

PATCHWORK pieces, plain and patterned,
Cottons, velvets, ginghams, satins,
Tacked to paper, stitched together
In each odd half-hour of leisure.
Every piece a memory of
A garment made with pride and love.

Rompers, dresses, shirts and trousers,
Nighties, 'jamas, skirts and blouses
Stitched while growing children slept,
Every remnant trimmed and kept.
Now the family's flown, and I
Have time I lacked in years gone by.

Time to cut and tack and sew
The quilt I dreamed of long ago,
While making up the cloth I bought
From market stalls for next to naught
And still each scrap is dear to me —
A patch of priceless memory.

— Jane Legge.

I wish he had six brothers, then his mother wouldn't think the sun rises and sets on him — and she might like me a bit better, too."

THE old lady was so startled by the outburst that she almost dropped her cup. Abruptly the girl got to her feet, clutching the baby.

"I'm sorry," she said, looking guilty. "I'm being stupid. It's just that I've been trying all day to get a baby-sitter — our regular one is ill."

"I don't see —" Agnes Benzie was bewildered.

"Ron's mother is in hospital and I can't take the baby. Tonight we have to go and see her. Last time I didn't go and Ron said she was annoyed." The dark eyes filled with angry tears.

"I never do the right thing. If I don't go, that's wrong, and if I do go, I shouldn't have left the baby!"

The older woman sat silent, because it was obvious all Jill Hunter needed was someone to listen to her.

"She never wanted us to get married in the first place. I wasn't good enough! I tried to make her like me. I really tried —" Jill broke off as the door opened. "Here's Ron now. Please don't say anything. I don't know what got into me. It just — all boiled over —"

"All's well." The young man was grinning. "You'd better leave a spare key with us or one of the other neighbours."

Ten minutes later, having expressed her thanks, Agnes Benzie crossed the now empty landing and reached the sanctuary of her own quiet flat, quiet except for the sounds made by her neighbours.

The People's Friend Annual

Now it wasn't just an assortment of noises, because she knew who was making them.

The radio next door was loud because the man Ron Hunter had called Sam Todd was deaf.

The heavy feet upstairs belonged to the painter and his family, and she had him to thank for making it possible for her to get into her flat.

The crying baby was the Hunters'.

The woman settled down later to finish her letter to Michael, reading over the stilted sentences, which held as much feeling as a grocery list. Her gaze drifted over to the framed photograph of her son, taken when he was dux of his school.

She had been so proud of him and wanted only the best for him. She bit her lip, troubled by thoughts which refused to go away. Was she like the mother-in-law of that girl across the way — possessive? Had it always been what she wanted for Michael that mattered, instead of what Michael wanted for himself?

Did Claire perhaps think of her in the same way as Jill did of Ron's mother? Did she think she never did anything right?

★　　　★　　　★　　　★

Agnes Benzie was a kind woman, for all her determination, and a fair woman, too. Once she began to doubt herself, she went on doing it. She knew in her heart she hadn't given Michael's wife a fair chance, not right from the beginning.

But Claire was Michael's choice and she would never know what Claire was really like if she remained a stranger.

Agnes tore the written sheet from the writing pad and started again. This time the words flowed more easily.

It seems a long time since I saw you. I hope you'll manage over soon — both of you — She thought for a moment and then carefully underlined the word *both.*

Once started, it was easy to tell the young people that she had locked herself out of her new flat and how helpful her new neighbours had all been.

I'm even baby-sitting tonight for Ron and Jill Hunter who live across the landing —

The bell rang and the woman laid aside the pad. She found her young neighbour on the step, her dark eyes troubled.

"I feel so ashamed, letting it all out on you about Ron's mother. I had no-one to talk to and it had been such a bad day, not being able to get a baby-sitter and the baby crying so much — and Ron's mother never understands. She never liked me —"

"Give her time." Agnes Benzie drew the girl into the house and closed the door. "Just give her time — and she'll learn."

The girl smiled.

"Do you really think so? You're such a comfort. You're going to be a marvellous new neighbour!"

"So are you," said the woman and knew she meant it. □

44

I See You Still

SOMETIMES, coming through the
door,
  I think I see you there,
Relaxing, so contentedly,
  In your favourite chair.

Your baccy-jar is on the shelf,
  And there it's going to stay,
I couldn't bear to part with it,
  No matter what folk say.

Your cherished pipe, your spectacles,
  Your books, your slippers, too.
In keeping them, I seem to keep
  A little bit of you.

These day-to-day, familiar things
  I now hold very dear,
For, in their simple homeliness,
  They seem to bring you near.

That's why I smile, much comforted,
  When coming through the door,
Because, deep in my heart, I know
  You've just gone on before!
                  — *Kathleen O'Farrell.*

SHADOW
ON THE SUN

by GRACE MACAULAY

BETH MORREN studied her husband's face gravely as she said in a quiet voice, "If you want to go on holiday by yourself — why not just say so — and go?"

Stan frowned, almost as if he were debating with himself rather than her.

"But I thought you might like to do the same. I thought it would be a break for you if your mother took the children."

Beth took a sip of her wine. A moment or two ago it had been sweet. Now it was clinging to her tongue with a strange bitterness. She answered Stan slowly.

"I would prefer to take the children to the caravan as usual." She kept herself from adding, "The children's holidays are very precious to me, if not to you."

Then she saw he was looking oddly disappointed, as if he had offered her a gift and she had rejected it. What sort of gift did he imagine it was, she wondered.

"I thought the idea would please you." He shrugged, looking slightly sullen as he went on, "I've been thinking about it a lot. I'm sure it would be good for both of us . . . *all* of us, I mean, of course," he finished lamely.

Beth put her hands on her lap under the table and clasped them, partly to stop them from shaking, partly to help her to pray inwardly for the wisdom to say the right thing.

"Naturally, I wouldn't try to keep you from making your own arrangements," she said. And then more firmly, "But I'd truly prefer to make my own decision."

She twisted her engagement and wedding rings round her finger, feeling the pain of the metal and stones digging into her flesh. Or perhaps, she thought, it was the pain in her heart shooting all through her body and finally lodging in the third finger of her left hand where the outward symbols of her love lived.

"Shall we have anything else?" Stan was looking at her enquiringly, as if continuing their meal was the most natural thing in the world.

"No . . ." she began, feeling that her head was too heavy to shake.

"Just coffee, then," Stan told the waiter smoothly.

An oppressive silence settled between them while they waited. Then Stan spoke with a mixture of exasperation and apology.

47

"It's not that much of a big deal, Beth. All I want is a couple of weeks of space — time to myself — to be me . . ."

She listened to him with a resigned detachment. What he was telling her was, in fact, that he wanted to be free of being a husband and father.

She forced her eyes away from his face and gazed around the restaurant. The decor was red and black, modern and yet traditional.

They wouldn't have bothered much with nights out, basically they were a home-loving couple, but Beth's mother had always insisted that young people ought to go out. Besides which, she enjoyed being alone with her grandchildren, getting to know them.

Beth knew that children tended to become different little people when they were out of their parents, immediate influence. She herself had been teaching now for a total of fourteen years. She knew precisely how long it was because the headmistress of the school was about to retire after forty-five years in teaching.

Somehow the shock figure of forty-five had set the rest of the staff counting up their own years of service and talking of retirement. One member of staff had mentioned interruptions to bring up children. But Beth didn't consider her maternity leaves to have been interruptions. She felt that, much as she enjoyed teaching, her true career was motherhood.

Gareth and Philip were eight and six years old now. In some ways she was sorry now that she had been so keen to get back to work after they were born. And she had experienced real regret when she had to go back three years ago after she had Jenny. But obviously her income was needed; she hadn't given herself a choice.

The family budget might have survived, but there would have been nothing left over for extras — such as dinner tonight. Not that this meal had been so very grand — not nearly as expensive as their last night out which had been to celebrate their ninth wedding anniversary.

STAN became silent now. And almost absently Beth spoke her thoughts aloud.

"I suppose this sort of thing ought to have happened two years ago."

Flushing, Stan protested. "But it's not like that, Beth! It's not anything like that seven-year-itch nonsense!

"I love you and I love the children as much as I ever did. Haven't you been listening? Can't I convince you that this is . . ."

"It sounds to me," Beth suggested slowly," that your need to get away is a symptom of some greater trouble."

"No!" He denied it positively. "As a matter of fact, the idea first came to me last year. I wanted to tell you about it — but time just sort of slipped by and then the summer was gone."

But Beth was past taking any of it in. His reasoning was too complex for her. Or perhaps she was too muddled to listen properly. She was shaking inside with anxiety to be home, to check that the children were fast asleep and safe from any possible harm.

Stan drove her mother home and when he returned Beth was in bed, lying curled up on her side, pretending to be asleep. Yet when Stan was making his own extra quiet preparations for bed, she was perversely, annoyed.

Surely he must know that she was only pretending to be asleep? Why didn't he say something? He must know that there was no way she would be able to sleep after that bombshell he had dropped!

Almost, she turned round. But she was imprisoned by her deep-rooted habit of calm. Not that calmness came naturally to her, for her earliest memories were of her mother scolding her and warning her.

"If you want to be a teacher, Beth, you must learn to control that temper of yours."

And her father advising her in milder tones.

"Beth, lass, what you must keep in mind is that anger invites anger. If you think something isn't right, or doesn't please you — then the best way to alter the situation is to have a quiet chat about it."

"But what if the other person doesn't listen?" Beth had demanded.

"Well, you listen carefully to the other person's point of view. Then you go away and have a think about it — decide where you might have common ground. And while you are doing all that — the heat goes out of your temper."

All her young life and for most of her adult life, Beth had struggled to keep tight reins on her volatile nature. So that even now, when the foundations of her marriage seemed to be crumbling, she exercised her self-control.

Naturally, she imagined that Stan and she would have some further discussion of his plans. But the following evening, he told her almost casually:

"I'm going up to the loft to organise my golfing gear. Some golf in sunny Spain seems like a good idea for a lone holiday."

And he went upstairs whistling merrily, apparently oblivious to her dismay.

THE next ten days were extremely busy for Beth. The last week of term meant lots of hustle and bustle in school while at home she had to keep things ticking over normally and also begin making some preparations for the holiday.

Four years ago they had decided to buy a caravan on a coastal site.

"It will be an investment," Stan had said. "No more plane or train tickets, or more having to get off the motorway because Philip is travel sick."

And after that first Easter holiday, they had congratulated each other jubilantly. The boys had enjoyed themselves enormously and so had they.

"Best of all." Beth had sighed happily on the way home." I'm not squirming at the memory of hotel guests saying 'Shhh' and giving our healthy boys black looks for raising their voices."

"Three cheers for the Morrens' holiday home!" Stan had urged the boys.

Beth Morren wasn't the type of person who tried to see into the

D
49

future. She lived very much in the present, and although she knew that time would bring gradual, natural changes, she had never anticipated any drastic alteration to her family life.

The children would grow up, Stan would probably be promoted from deputy head to headmaster of the school where he taught or some other school in the district — they'd already decided they would never want to move.

She was twenty-five when she married Stan Morren. He was thirty-five but the age difference meant nothing to them. Their rapturous love convinced them that they were twin souls who had been waiting to find each other.

Together, they had created their own ideal world — finding pleasure in their children and in the ordinary things of life.

And now Beth felt betrayed and unable to think clearly. Her anger had evaporated, leaving her with an empty sensation that was almost like fear.

★　　　★　　　★　　　★

At the breakfast table on the morning of their departure for the caravan, she experienced the eerie sensation that she was playing out a charade for the last time.

After today nothing would ever be the same for any of them.

"Honey on my toast, please." Jenny smiled her sweet angelic smile.

"Certainly, darling." Beth's features relaxed fondly as she looked at her tiny three-year-old daughter. She spread honey on a piece of toast and cut it into neat fingers, murmuring softly, "There you are."

At the same time eight-year-old Gareth asked:

"Daddy, will you take us fishing whenever we arrive — or must we help with the unpacking first?"

Beth's eyes flew to her husband's face. He was looking at their son with a mixture of tolerance and amusement as he replied:

"You are forgetting, Gareth — I'm not coming with you to the caravan this time."

"Why not?" Gareth was bewildered. And he added, "You can't stay at home all by yourself."

"No, of course I'm not staying here." His father smiled, and reminded him, "I told you — I'm going to Spain."

"*What*?" Gareth's face turned pale and his eyes widened and glittered with accusation. "You said you would take me to Spain! You said you would take me to all the places on the photographs I don't remember because I was too little and Philip was only a baby."

▶ *p52*

The main road that winds alongside "the bonnie bonnie banks of Loch Lomond" passes through the little village of Luss. With its idyllic situation the village is a favourite stopping place for visitors — never more so than in summer when it plays host to one of the smaller Highland Gatherings.

LUSS and LOCH LOMOND : J CAMPBELL KERR

"Yes, I know I've said that," his father replied patiently, "but I meant someday — I didn't mean this year . . ."

"But that's not fair! Is it, Philip?" He turned to his brother for support, demanding insistently, "Didn't he promise? Didn't he, Philip? Didn't he?"

Philip nodded. His manner was milder and quieter than Gareth's. But his shocked face made it obvious that he shared his brother's amazement and outrage.

"I'm sorry if you misunderstood," their father began — and paused to look at their mother as if for confirmation.

Beth's gaze met his for an instant before she looked away, unable to take part in the argument. Then her stomach muscles tightened into knots as she heard Gareth's howl of vexation.

"I did not misunderstood!" Gareth threw himself out of his chair. The table rocked dangerously. His mug of milk went flying. Milk splashed on Jenny and she began to cry.

But Gareth did not notice. In frenzied rage he continued to shout incoherent protests at his father.

"Now, Gareth, that's enough!" Stan Morren grew stern. "Sit down and finish your breakfast . . ."

"I will not! I hate my breakfast! I won't eat it! And I won't go to the caravan! I want to go to Spain."

Gareth's tantrum increased in momentum while he spoke. He was hopping from one foot to the other as if the floor beneath him was on fire. His face was scarlet. Tears spouted from his eyes and as he tried to wipe them away with the palms of his hands he seemed to be violently slapping his own face.

Beth made a move towards him. But Stan was quicker. He rose to his feet and lifted Gareth into his arms. And regardless of flailing arms and kicking feet, he hugged the boy tightly to his breast and carried him out of the room.

JENNY was frightened. She was wailing loudly as she scrambled down from the table to be caught up in her mother's arms.

Beth soothed her automatically. But her thoughts were with Gareth. She knew that his father would hold him lovingly and reassuringly until he was calm. But Beth knew exactly how frightened Gareth must have been when his temper boiled and exploded out of control. And she knew all too well the feelings of misery and shame he would suffer later.

Poor Gareth, she felt an ache of sympathy in her heart for him — it was going to be so difficult for him to learn to curb his temper.

Then six-year-old Philip suddenly spoke in a voice filled with admiration.

"I wish I had a temper like Gareth's."

Beth began to say, "Philip, don't be silly." But she paused, astonished by the shining hero-worship in his eyes.

She realised that Philip was not being silly. He truly did admire, and perhaps envy his older brother's ability to storm and rage.

She said gently, "Gareth will be sad about losing his temper."

"I know." Philip sighed. "But I wouldn't be. If it was me I would be glad. I think it must be great to be able to stick up for yourself."

"But there are other ways," his mother reminded him. "Surely you wouldn't want to have tantrums? You can speak out when you like, can't you?"

She hadn't raised her voice, nor sounded scolding. But he lowered his eyes and closed his lips tightly, as if firmly retreating from her.

She sighed, thinking that Gareth would have been willing to talk the matter out. But Philip did not have the confidence. She must discuss this with Stan and together they would find ways to build up the child's confidence and self-esteem. Perhaps during the holiday . . .

Her thoughts halted abruptly and her throat tightened with pain as tears burned at the back of her eyes.

Setting Jenny down on the floor, she suggested brightly, "How about you and Philip helping me to clear the table?"

A SHORT while later, Stan returned alone. Beth glanced at him enquiringly but he sent the children upstairs before he said anything.

"Gareth is all right now. I've explained to him . . ."

"Have you indeed?" Something in his quiet tones infuriated Beth. She turned her back on him and rattled the dishes noisily in the sink.

"Careful, Beth. You'll break something," he warned her.

"OK! You wash up!" Beth did not look at him as she flung out of the kitchen and ran upstairs, calling out to the children at the top of her voice.

"Right, everybody! Time to leave now! Who wants to go to the seaside?"

There was a burst of activity and noise as they collected their various belongings. But the leave-taking, especially the parting from Stan was extremely subdued and low key.

Beth thought the children must be sharing her own feelings of gloomy unreality, because there was scarcely a sound from any of them until they arrived at the caravan site. Her spirits were at their lowest ebb as she parked the car and unfastened her seat-belt.

There were eight caravans on the site and it was quite usual for parents to arrive singly with the children. Nobody was likely to comment on Stan's absence, she realised, as she watched the children scampering away to be greeted by their holiday friends.

▶ *p56*

Surrounded by the rich Herefordshire farmland, the small town of Ledbury is a delightful place. It features many black and white houses and inns, of which the 17th century Market House is particularly striking. There are associations with John Masefield, the Poet Laureate, and Elizabeth Barrett Browning in this lovely, unspoilt corner of England.

LEDBURY, Herefordshire : J CAMPBELL KERR

The sky above the sea was grey blue and hazy, the air was warm, the musical sound of childish laughter followed her as she went to open up the caravan. The day would have been perfect if only Stan were here, she thought — but the summer was marred for her before it began.

Yet she must not let it be spoilt for the children, she decided. That would be cruel. For their sake, she must pretend that everything was fine and get on with enjoying the holiday and routine of life in the caravan.

For the rest of the day, she managed to keep to her resolve. But when she lay awake alone in the darkness of the night she was overwhelmed by panic and despair and the tortures of self-doubt. She must have driven Stan away. She had made him unhappy. She had failed him somewhere . . .

★   ★   ★   ★

In the morning when she woke, little Jenny was sitting beside her on Stan's pillow. When Beth opened her eyes, Jenny gave her an angelic smile and continued to sing in her high sweet voice a song she had learned at nursery school.

It was a good beginning to the day, Beth thought, as she reached out to stroke her tiny daughter's silky curls.

After breakfast, Beth sat at the edge of the shore watching the children building a sand castle. The sun was hot, already her energy was draining away.

She would simply sit here for most of the day . . . and the next day, and the day after that.

She was only vaguely aware of a moving shadow on the sand on the fourth day of the holiday. The children were building another castle. And as they came running towards her shouting frantically she thought for a second that something was wrong.

Then suddenly she could clearly hear what they were shouting.

"Daddy! Daddy! Daddy . . ."

She felt dizzy for a moment as she turned to see Stan standing close to her. Their eyes met for an instant, then he was stooping down to gather the children close to him as they laughed and squealed with excitement when he assured them over and over again that he had missed them too much to stay away from them any longer.

Beth was content to watch and listen. Content because in that single glance Stan had seemed to tell her so much. Perhaps she would never fully understand the need which had prompted him to want some freedom. But one thing she did know, and that for certain — their love was intact.

She knew also that she had been wise to stifle her temper and let him go without a fuss. Soon the parting and these four days of heartache would fade from her mind. But somehow she thought that the bonds which held them together had been tested and strengthened.

Finally the children returned to their play and he came to sit beside her. She looked at him wordlessly. Then he held out his hand and she took it and their fingers intertwined. □

MAISIE LEE stood looking down at the white envelope before she bent and picked it up.

For weeks now the streets had been festooned with fairy lights. The stores were bright with colour and Father Christmas grottoes had sprung up in competition with each other, to the bewilderment of the children — and the despair of their parents.

A Christmas Blessing

by
MARY
LEDGWAY

So far Maisie had managed to close her door and leave all signs of Christmas outside, but now, with this card, Christmas had come into her home. It was not a card chosen with love for someone dear, just a kindly thought from a neighbour, but the gold lettering of the simple greeting made her realise that she could no longer shut her eyes to the festive season.

Maisie sat on a stool in front of the newly-lit fire. Her first Christmas without Len. She wasn't bitter — they'd had many happy years together, more than most, but the sense of emptiness, the loneliness, was a persistent ache.

Her eyes fell on the patchwork cover on Len's chair. It had started life as the centrepiece for a quilt, but when she'd spread it on the chair to have a look at it, Len had suggested it stayed there.

"All that work and it will hardly be seen upstairs. Let it be, lass."

Over the years the cover had taken on the shape of the old chair. Now Maisie's eyes went to the small square of rose-pink crepe. Her wedding dress.

Her sister had made it. Hours of work in the rouleau and tiny covered buttons. Had she ever thanked her, Maisie wondered, remembering how much the young take things for granted.

It was a wartime wedding. Len had three days' leave and they had been married early in the morning so they didn't waste any of their precious time together. Maisie remembered the desolation she felt as she walked away from the train that was carrying Len away from her.

She had wanted to follow her sister into the Forces, but her parents needed her and so she joined the staff of a nearby hospital. She recalled her tears that first day as she helped with the dressing on a small boy's leg.

Sister had taken her to one side.

"Tears won't help him, nurse. Just do the job."

At the time Maisie had thought Sister hard and uncaring, but had soon come to know her as one of the most compassionate people she would ever meet.

Yes, she thought now, as her finger touched the square of heavy blue cotton. She had been proud of her uniform.

Then came the news that Len was on his way home.

Spending most of her time in uniform, Maisie had given away most of her clothing coupons but Granny Wood had come to the rescue with a length of carefully hoarded flowered curtaining. From somewhere her mother found a top to match, but when Len took her in his arms it wouldn't have mattered if she had been wearing sackcloth.

Then, that evening, they'd gone dancing. The curtain skirt swirled out and it was as if their happiness would last for ever.

But the years passed and the children they longed for didn't arrive. In fact, Maisie was well into the thirties when first Robin, than Katie made their much-wanted appearance. Maisie loved motherhood, and her children adored her.

The scrap of white lace from the christening gown, though yellowed with time, was oh so, precious.

A Christmas Blessing

Then Maisie's eyes saddened as they rested on a scrap of blue striped shirting. Denzil! Suddenly the years rolled away . . .

R OBIN was ten when Maisie learned that a dear friend of her mother's was dying alone in a London hospital. Although she dreaded the journey Maisie went to her, and the look in Daisy Whiteley's eyes was reward enough.

As she sat there Maisie became aware of the lady in the next bed who was weeping quietly into her pillow.

"It's her children," Daisy whispered. "Mrs Brent — Kathleen — has to have an operation and there is no-one to care for them. She is afraid that if they go into care she may not get them back."

The next day when Maisie went in there were two children by Kathleen Brent's bed. The boy stood proud and tall, his deep grey eyes quietly accepting what was to come, but the girl sobbed.

"It's all right, Paula," the boy comforted. "I'll look after you."

Maisie saw the struggle Kathleen Brent was having not to break down in front of the children. Saw that the boy's shirt, although much too big, was spotlessly clean as was the faded cotton dress showing below the thin cardigan of the girl. She saw their pale cheeks and thought of her own two children, rosy and fit with fresh air and good food. She knew what she had to do . . .

It was late when they all reached Maisie's home at Bronhurst. She fed the children dripping toast and chocolate cake and tucked them into bed. The money for their fares had taken all she had, but she knew she had done the right thing, and Len — understanding Len — agreed with her.

▶ *over*

according to Custom

I T'S pure chance that Valentine's Day is associated with the priest, St Valentine, as the custom had nothing to do with him apart from the fact that it takes place on his day. It was, in fact, several centuries ago that young people in England and Scotland began sending each other secret romantic messages on that day. The idea of sending lace-edged cards really became popular about one hundred years ago.

The children loved the quiet Yorkshire village. Paula and Katie, much of an age, became good friends. And Denzil?

Did her own children ever resent what Maisie felt for Denzil? No, she thought, for Denzil did not take the love that was theirs. He made his own place in her heart, and in her home.

Maisie remembered how the other children had looked up to him. His quiet, calming influence on her own two boisterous offspring, his love of all things beautiful. Yet he was not without spirit enough to fight when it was needed.

Maisie had bathed his cuts when he came home and Robin had looked at him seriously.

"I thought you didn't fight!"

"Sometimes you have to. When you know it is the only way, and you know that what you're fighting for is right."

How often had Denzil's grey eyes met hers across the room? How often they had shared a silent joke and how many the times they had sat together talking as Denzil grew older.

Even after their mother was well and made a cosy home for them, the children came to Maisie for the summer holidays. Then, when Denzil was almost seventeen, Kathleen Brent died as quietly as she had lived.

★   ★   ★   ★

Maisie and Len thought the children would stay with them, but an uncle turned up out of the blue and whisked them off to America.

"Never could get on with our Kath," he said, "but I might make something of the children."

Oh, there had been a few letters, but gradually they had dwindled to nothing. Maisie had written, but reading back over her badly-written lines, recognising the spelling was poor, she had torn them up.

Len or Robin would have written for her, but she didn't know how to say what she wanted through a third person. She only knew the ache in her heart for Denzil did not grow less. That she missed him more than ever now she was alone.

Now she would have to face a Christmas not only without those she had lost, but it seemed without her own children.

Robin, married and living about five miles away, was usually a constant visitor. His two children adored Nana, and she in her turn often went to Robin's. However, it was a long time since she had seen him — not since Christmas came near.

Katie, working now, had a small flat on the outskirts of a nearby town. It was rare that a week went by without her little car drawing up outside her mother's house, but now almost three had gone past.

True, the children had asked them over on other Christmases, but Len's failing health had meant they were better at home. Now it looked as though the young ones preferred their own company.

A falling coal disturbed the stillness, and Maisie rose and made herself a coffee.

Then she decided to take away some of her gloom by going out. She caught a bus into town and did her shopping, choosing her gifts and cards with the care she always showed.

IT was three days before Christmas when Robin came. Maisie was disappointed when no small children tumbled out of the car after him.

"Mum! No Christmas tree?" he said, stepping into the sitting-room. "We must put that right."

Maisie said nothing as Robin climbed up to the top cupboard and pulled down the boxes of trimmings. She didn't stop him dashing out to the market garden or show any enthusiasm as he proudly showed her the small bushy tree he had bought.

If Robin noticed her lack of interest he didn't say anything and whistled cheerfully as he tied on the baubles. Lastly he fixed the silver angel in position on the top branch. An angel with a broken wing, but one that had topped the tree as long as he could remember.

"There now!"

He looked round with a smile. The tree stood in the corner it had always stood in. Holly was perched behind the pictures and strands of silver festooned the window.

"That's better! I must go now, Mum. See you!"

He bent and kissed her and Maisie was alone again. The Christmas decorations did nothing to lighten her heart.

Katie came on Christmas Eve. She knelt by her mother and handed her a package.

"Your Christmas present. But you can open it now. Go on."

Maisie drew out the blue dress. The silk skirt fell in

Winter Dreams

WINTER is for dreaming
Of all that might have been,
And those we've loved, whose memory
For ever will be green.
For on chilly winter evenings,
When all is dark and drear,
Old friends seem doubly precious,
And bygone days more dear.
That's why, when nimble fingers
Bedeck the yuletide bough,
Comrades from the long ago
Seem very close, somehow.
And though the wind may bluster
Upon a snow-bound night,
The moon seems twice as luminous,
The starshine twice as bright.

Winter is for dreaming,
For sweet remembering,
And a time for looking forward
To the golden days of spring!
— *Kathleen O'Farrell.*

soft folds, the white lace collar was delicate, the sleeves long with tiny frills at the cuffs.

"Try it on," Katie insisted.

It fitted perfectly and in spite of herself Maisie felt a little glow of pleasure when she saw her reflection. When she would have taken it off, though, Katie told her to keep it on.

"We're going to church. There will be carols, you'll like that."

The church was almost full, but Katie led her mother to the front.

Maisie could only stare as Robin moved up to make room for her. In front of them Fiona, Robin's wife, sat with the two children. Then the organ began to play.

They walked slowly down the far aisle, then turned up the centre one.

Beside their own elderly clergyman walked a younger one, and as he came level with Maisie he paused. She looked up and found herself looking into dark grey eyes — caring eyes.

She saw a gentle mouth curved into a smile of greeting, and then he was walking away. Maisie looked up at Robin, saw his smile, she felt Katie's hand on hers and knew they understood.

M AISIE watched as Denzil walked up the steps to the pulpit. For a moment or two the church was quiet, then slowly he began to speak.

"Some of you may remember me as a boy among you, some may not. I am honoured that your vicar has asked me to talk to you this evening. Christmas time, when all of you give unstintingly of both time and money to others. But how many of us carry the true Christian spirit with us through the year?

"I am thinking of an ordinary housewife, not rich in this world's goods, but rich in the true meaning of Christianity. She opened her heart and her home to two frightened, lonely children . . ."

The rest of the service was a blur to Maisie. Then she was home and her children were lifting food out of their cars, covering the table.

"I couldn't let you talk to the children," Robin explained. "They would have let the secret out . . . Denzil wanted to get in touch, but he did not know whether we were still here, so he wrote to the vicar.

"Katie did most of the work in between the office's Christmas rush. Tomorrow you are all coming to Fiona and me, and on Boxing Day Katie is doing the honours."

Then it was time to take the children home. All of a sudden, the laughter and the noise of the evening quietened — and Maisie was alone with Denzil.

He came and knelt beside her.

"I'm sorry, Mother Mai!" The old pet name slipped out as naturally as it had come into use, years before, and Maisie smiled.

"Sorry?" she queried.

"For not writing — for not keeping in touch. America was a completely new way of life. Uncle wanted so much of me. For a while I thought that was what I wanted, too, then one day I escaped from the hurly-burly and went fishing on a quiet lake.

"The peace and tranquillity gradually enveloped me, and I found myself remembering my old values, the happiness of simple things.

"My uncle was annoyed at first, then he helped me all he could. He still had Paula and she loved his way of life. She will be coming to see you next summer, with a brand new husband.

"Uncle sent me to one of the best theological colleges, and I knew it was the right thing for me.

A Christmas Blessing

"Then, when I was ordained, I closed me eyes for the blessing and suddenly all the pomp, the majesty of my surroundings, the gleaming silver and the rich vestments, faded. I was back in the grey stone village church at Bronhurst. You were holding my hand, telling me when to sit, when to kneel.

"I knew then that whatever blessing I received from the church, my new life would not be complete without your blessing, Mother Mai. Dear Mother Mai!"

So Maisie Lee, an ordinary housewife, who had never travelled, never written a cheque, never delved into any of life's mysteries, laid her work-worn hand on the bent head of the boy she loved so dearly, and in the quiet of her own home gently, sincerely, gave him her blessing. For a few minutes there was silence, then the clock struck and Denzil looked up.

"Happy Christmas, Mother Mai." He grinned. He delved into his jacket pocket and handed her a small package. From the bright wrappings Maisie drew a shimmering Christmas angel.

"Yours on one condition," he teased. "I have the old one."

He took the old angel down and his eyes were tender as he put it carefully to one side. So many memories.

"I'm hungry!" he announced suddenly. "Couldn't eat much earlier."

"I couldn't either," admitted Maisie ruefully.

"Dripping toast," queried Denzil, looking at the red cinders glowing in the open grate.

Mother Mai shook her head.

"Honey," she suggested.

"And chocolate cake?"

Maisie laughed and began to hum, "If I'd know you were coming . . ."

"Frozen chocolate eclairs?"

"Smashing! You cut the bread. I'll make the toast . . ." ☐

IT was a cold, blustery day and Calum Clark's mother was just getting over an attack of flu. After a busy spell of selling for his firm, Calum had come home to find her looking "wabbit," as she termed it.

Marion Clark was annoyed with herself. She had hoped to be back on her feet, fully recovered by this time, but here she was, Calum home and she hardly able to look after him.

There was a long list of shopping to be done and the prospect worried her.

"Cheer up, I'll get it for you," her son offered that first morning. "Buying is a lot easier than selling! Just give me your list. I'll take it to the wee shop at the corner. Nothing to it!"

His mother shook her head.

"The wee shop won't do, Calum," she told him. "You'll have to go to the supermarket."

"So we've got a supermarket now, have we?" he queried.

"Yes, in the Square. It really is super, Calum. And such a choice!" Her son looked doubtful.

"I've never been in one of those places. I wouldn't know what to do."

She reassured him. "It's easy. You just take a trolley and go round and help yourself. Nothing could be simpler."

"Oh, all right." Never let it be said that Calum Clark lacked the spirit of adventure! He read over the list.

"Must I take a shopping bag?"

"Take the car, there's a good car park. Nobody need see you, if that's what you're afraid of."

"I'm not afraid," he assured her. "Here goes, then! I'll be as quick as I can."

He gave her a kiss on the cheek and she waved to him as he drove off.

FINDING the supermarket was simple. In the old-fashioned Square, it stood out in all its newness. So far, so good. Parking the car, Calum walked through the portals of what was to him strange territory.

The place was unbelievably large. He felt almost dizzy at the impact of countless displays of every kind of foodstuff imaginable. Counters of fruit, bakeries, meat and groceries, the aisles between packed with customers looking very grim and intent as they made their choice and filled their trolleys.

by MARY DUNN

When Calum Went Shopping!

He would have to use a trolley, he supposed. Disentangling one from the stacking row, he began his journey. They were awkward things to wheel, he found, or perhaps it was just himself that was awkward.

Self-consciously he helped himself to a melon, a box of dates and a bag of potatoes, then took a sharp turn towards the breakfast foods.

At that moment another trolley came swerving towards him, to shudder into his with a noisy crash . . .

Calum stood red faced. Then he noticed that the other trolley was being clutched by a small boy with a round, mischievous face.

He put out a hand to steady it.

"That's a heavy load, son! Where's your mother?"

A girl came hurrying towards them.

"Robin, you scallywag!" She turned to Calum. "He ran away with the trolley, I'm afraid. Any harm done?"

Calum looked down into a pair of very blue eyes. "None whatever. I can't handle these things, I'm afraid."

The blue eyes twinkled. "You're doing quite well. I've been watching you. Your first time, is it?"

He nodded. "For my mother. She's ill."

"Too bad. Can I do anything to help?"

It was too good a chance to miss.

"There's a special marmalade she likes. I can't see it anywhere."

"I'll have a look. Robin, stand by that trolley and don't move an inch!"

She went with Calum to another part of the store where they traced the marmalade with no trouble. Then she gave him clues about finding his other errands, before going her own way.

After that, everything was easy and he returned in triumph to the nearest check-out.

Just in front of him he saw Robin and his blue-eyed mother. They exchanged smiles, like old friends.

The store was much less frightening now. He watched while she unloaded her trolley and packed her purchases into two plastic bags. They were so heavy she could hardly lift them.

"How are you going to get these home?" he asked.

"There's a Payphone just outside," she told him. "I'll get a taxi."

Calum made an impulsive decision.

"I've got a car outside. I can give you a lift."

She hesitated. It was Robin who replied — gleefully.

"Yes, please! You know we're in a hurry, Betsy!"

Betsy? So she *wasn't* his mother after all. He studied the smiling face, the red-gold hair and blue eyes and his heart, or something, gave a leap.

"It's no trouble," he added quickly. "Honestly."

"Well, thank you," she conceded. "You're a godsend, really."

"And you have been a godsend to me."

L ADEN with their purchases, they made their way out to the car. It turned out that her name was Betsy Lennox and Robin was her nephew.

"I'm staying with my sister for a while," she explained. "She's not

Song Of Crete

MOUNTAINS stand against vivid sky,
Blue water shimmers in breathless heat,
Hibiscus colours walls of white,
And sands beneath the tamarisks are dark
With bodies sacrificed to the great god Sun.

On a multi-coloured graffitied wall
A yellow bird sings, in a wooden cage,
In competition with Cretan song.
Chickens cluck amongst the stones,
Feathers away from death by motor-scooter.

In a bamboo'd waterside taverna
The smell of coffee, and sea-bream cooking.
And in bars beside the deep dark lake in town
A peasant offers sage for sale,
Its strange perfume intoxicates the soul.

English tastebuds tuned to tea and strawberry jam
Venture gaily into unknown worlds of food and wine,
And sample tasty Greek delights,
Yoghurt with honey, baclava
And feta cheese, olives and ouzo.

Beneath searching fingertips the feel of ancient times,
Marble and gypsum resurrected.
Ripe figs rot in corners, fir cones found on royal paths,
A palmful of stones, brought home
To work their magic.

Senses defined, evoked with ease,
But something more is there in Crete,
A sense of wonder.

— *June Picken.*

doing much shopping at the moment."

Robin put in — "Tell him about the new baby!"

She laughed. "Yes, there was a new baby last week. A girl."

"And what does Robin think about that?" he queried.

The boy pondered. "Well, a brother would have been better," he admitted, "but I'll make do. The others seem to be pleased."

Calum laughed. "You'll change your mind about girls, my lad!"

Betsy and Robin proved such good company that the journey to their trim little bungalow passed in a twinkling. They stood and waved to him on the step before going inside, their faces bright and laughing.

Calum felt a warm glow and was still smiling when he reached home.

"You've been a long time," remarked his mother. "Did you get everything?"

"Absolutely. Even the marmalade."

"Good. By the way, Cousin Beatrice rang. She's coming along tonight with Marjorie." Her voice had a meaningful ring.

Cousin Beatrice was not really a cousin, just an old friend. Marjorie, her daughter, and Calum had been childhood friends. He suspected that the two mothers had plans for them.

"You will be nice to Marjorie?" ventured Mrs Clark.

"Of course I'll be nice. What do you take me for?"

"Sorry. I meant specially nice. You do think a lot of her, don't you?"

He gave her a warning look. "Mother, what are you getting at?"

"Nothing at all. Well, all right then. Don't you think you've been a bachelor long enough, Calum?"

He chuckled. "I'm quite happy as a bachelor, thank you. Some day I'll probably get married, but get this into your head, Mum. I like Marjorie quite well, but not in the way you mean. She's not the kind of girl I fancy as a wife."

"Oh." She eyed him narrowly. "You've got somebody in mind, then."

No harm in letting her think so, he reflected.

"Well, perhaps."

"You might have told me. What is she like, this girl, Calum?"

A picture suddenly flashed into his mind.

"Well, she — she's got red hair. Not very red, more goldy," he replied dreamily. "A smiling face with a pokey wee chin and the bluest eyes you ever saw."

His mother looked disbelieving.

"You're making her up. She sounds the helpless sort. Now Marjorie is anything but helpless. She's very fond of you, Calum. Probably in love with you."

"Oh, goodness, I hope not!" he exclaimed. "I'm not worth it."

All the same, the thought began to worry him and it made him feel extremely self-conscious that evening when Marjorie and her mother arrived.

MARJORIE was a tall, good-looking girl with dark eyes and firm features. She taught in the local college and was in demand as a speaker on women's topics.

She was never at a loss for a word and Calum had always enjoyed her company. But as for being in love with her, definitely no, and he hoped his mother was mistaken about her feelings.

The thought sprang back as he shook hands with Marjorie. Was the pressure of her largish hand, he wondered, just too close and warm for mere friendship?

"Calum, it seems like years since you were home! We've missed you."

"I've missed you, too," he replied, hoping she wouldn't read more into that than he meant.

Though he told himself not to be foolish, the thought recurred throughout the evening, especially when the two mothers drifted from the room to examine the new kitchen units, leaving the young couple together. He guessed they had done it on purpose, but Marjorie seemed quite at ease.

In fact, she was so pleasant to him he began to wish he could find it possible to fall in love.

"Marjorie," he remarked, "I — you — we were really good friends when we were kids, weren't we?"

"The best, Calum. We still are, aren't we?" She beamed at him.

"Sure," he agreed, and just then the mothers came in, giving them a meaningful glance.

Calum was very relieved when the two visitors took their leave.

His mother seemed quite pleased with the visit.

"I'm glad you got on so well with Marjorie, Calum! It was easy to see she was smitten."

according to Custom

ONE of Jersey's many summer attractions is its annual Battle of Flowers which dates from the island's celebrations of the Coronation of Edward VII and Queen Alexandra at the turn of the century. Today this floral extravaganza is a mile-long procession through the streets of St Helier — its decorated floats made up from millions of multi-coloured blooms

"Nonsense, Mother," He felt quite angry. "I told you!"

He strode off bedward . . . hating the very idea that any girl should be "smitten" by him — except the right girl, of course, and he hadn't met her yet, had he?

Next morning, his mother's first words of greeting were:

"A fine shopper you are! You forgot to get salt."

"Really?" He clapped his hand to his head. "Then I'd better go and get it today."

"Yes, but you needn't go to the supermarket. The corner shop will do."

But Calum took the car and went to the supermarket. There was a chance that Betsy might be there again — just a passing thought!

There was no sign of her, however. He wasted a lot of time finding the salt, hoping she would appear. But even if she did, she'd probably be quite different today, he thought gloomily, not his kind of girl at all.

He made his purchase at last and was on his way to the check-out when he saw her. She was alone today and in every way she was as enchanting as he remembered her. More so, in fact.

HELLO, there!" His voice betrayed his delight.

"You're back. What did you forget?" she teased.

He told her. "Get your stuff and I'll wait for you."

She told him it wasn't really necessary, she had very little to carry. But he took no notice, just waited and then, without protest, ran her home.

Before they parted he had decided they would have to meet again.

"Betsy, I'll be going away soon. I'd love to take you out somewhere first. I'm not much use at dances and things! What would you like to do?"

The blue eyes twinkled. "It's kind of you, Calum, but I'm really booked up."

"I don't believe you. It's just that we don't really know each other, isn't it?"

She laughed. "Not really. I know who you are and all about you. It's a small town, this."

"Well, who'd have thought it! OK, then, cancel one of your bookings."

"Just like that? Oh, well," she conceded. "You can buy one of my tickets for the concert in the town hall on Saturday."

Calum went home triumphant.

"I'm taking that girl to the concert on Saturday," he informed his mother.

She looked startled. "What girl, Calum?"

"The one I told you about. Red hair, blue eyes."

She still looked disbelieving. "I thought you'd be taking Marjorie to the concert. I'm sure she was expecting you to ask her."

Country Garden

THE trees that guard the garden
   Are dressed in varied greens,
Now gilding to autumnal
   Of gold and russet scenes.

The last red rose of summer
   Smiles brightly from her stem,
Exhales nostalgic perfume.
   A solitary gem.

Brown thrushes, sparrows, blackbirds
   Are scattered on the lawn.
They search for worms for breakfast
   This cool October morn.

A windmill in the distance,
   Wood galleried, looks down
On tranquil, dreaming country,
   Not very far from town.

— Margaret Comer.

70

When Calum Went Shopping

"Rubbish, Mother." But he had an uneasy feeling she might be right.

On Saturday, however, the sight of Betsy waiting for him at the bungalow banished all other thoughts.

She was wearing a dress and jacket of pale yellow and her hair was sunny, too. He seemed to have known her for a very long time, they were so at ease with each other . . . And to think they might never have met if he hadn't gone to the supermarket!

Once inside the town hall, they joined the crowd and began to make for their seats. Suddenly Calum drew in his breath.

There, practically at his elbow, was Marjorie herself, beaming at him.

"Well, Calum, I didn't expect to see you here!" Then her eye lit on his companion. "And you're not alone, either. Well, neither am I. This is Andrew Blair — remember him?"

Calum had not noticed the tall, good-looking young man till now. They nodded to each other. They had been schoolmates, Calum recalled, and Andrew had been sweet on Marjorie. He looked as if he was still sweet on her.

In fact, he had a proprietory air which could only mean one thing. Happily, he introduced Betsy and they took their seats.

Never had Calum enjoyed a concert so much, though the actual events remained very vague in his mind. The reason of course was Betsy, sitting so close he could feel the delicate perfume of her hair and smile down into her eyes.

Altogether, it was a perfect evening. Afterwards as they sat in the car at her gate, he said:

"I'll phone you tomorrow. Will you come for tea and meet my mother some day soon? I've told her about you."

Betsy dimpled. "How precipitate, Calum, but yes, I'll come."

Her nearness was too much for him and he drew her even closer.

The kiss he gave her was not very expert but she seemed to like it.

"I hope your mother will approve of me," she murmured.

"How could she help it?" he demanded.

★　　　★　　　★　　　★

Marion Clark was still up when Calum got home.

'Was it a good concert?" she asked.

"Terrific," he replied. "by the way, Marjorie was there. She had a man with her — Andrew Blair. He seemed pretty taken with her."

She shook her head at him. "Oh, Calum, you've missed the boat. It might have been you!"

"I didn't want it to be me! I was with Betsy. Yes, and she's coming for tea, so you can meet her."

Marion drew a deep breath. "So she is real!"

"Delightfully real." He treated her to a loving hug.

Marion Clark had never seen her son like this before — as if a light had been lit deep inside him.

She sighed contentedly. Oh well, if this Betsy could do that, she must be all right — perhaps even better for him than Marjorie. □

by
JEAN MELVILLE

GETTING
TO
KNOW
YOU

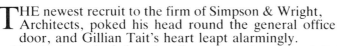

T HE newest recruit to the firm of Simpson & Wright,
Architects, poked his head round the general office
door, and Gillian Tait's heart leapt alarmingly.

She had worked for the firm ever since she left her
commercial college three years ago, but when old Mr Wright
died, the Simpson brothers had taken on a new partner, Charles
Bell.

From the first, Gillian had been attracted by Charles Bell's dark good
looks which she thought were only enhanced by the reserve in him.
Even when she learned from their receptionist that he was married with
a little girl, that attraction refused to go away — much to her own
inward annoyance.

There would be no happy future for her if she fell in love with Charles
Bell!

"Ah, there you are, Miss Tait," he said now, with one of his rare
smiles. "Before the hubbub of the day, could I ask a special favour?"

"Certainly, Mr Bell."

He handed her a small notice.

"Could you run off copies of this on the photocopier please? Would
two hundred be too many?"

She studied the notice which was an announcement that a small lilac-

point Siamese kitten had been lost, and that a reward would be paid if returned to the address given.

"It was given to my daughter, Mandy, by my mother for her fifth birthday," he told her awkwardly. "Name of Misty. I hope to interest our Cubs in distributing the notices through letterboxes. Mandy is upset, and surely someone must have seen the animal."

"I'm so sorry your daughter's cat is lost, Mr Bell," Gillian said.

He was an aloof man, but it was obvious that he doted on his small daughter. His wife sounded a calm, charming lady, however. She sometimes rang the office and Gillian had switched the call through to his private office. So far she had not stooped low enough to listen in!

His eyes were lingering on her face and she wondered if he realised that his show of interest in her, at times, did not help at all. It was always unexpected and disconcerting.

"I'll run these off for you, Mr Bell," she said crisply. "I hope you find the kitten."

"Thank you, Miss Tait. You're very kind and helpful."

★　　　★　　　★　　　★

It was almost a week later that Gillian pricked up her ears when she heard an interesting conversation at the corner shop on her way to work. She had called in to buy coffee and a tin of biscuits for the office, and found Mr Bryson serving an elderly woman.

"Oh, I'll have another of those small tins of catfood, Mr Bryson," she was saying. "The wee cat likes it very much. Yes, she's settling down fine but she was a poor wet thing when I got her. I've called her Silver."

"Very good, Mrs Cameron. I'll deliver these home for you if you like."

Gillian hesitated only for a second.

"Pardon me, but it's not a wee Siamese kitten you've got, by any chance?" she asked.

The old lady looked at her slightly startled.

"What? Oh . . . oh no, it's not a Siamese cat. I know fine what they look like. It's a nice little cat, though, and great company."

Gillian nodded somewhat disappointedly. She would dearly like to have returned to the office to tell Mr Bell she had found Mandy's cat!

A FEW days later Gillian learned that Mandy was put to bed with a bad cold, having been found wandering in the garden in her flimsy nightdress, looking for Misty.

"Miss Tait," Charles Bell said briskly after he had arrived the following morning, "could you please contact the Allendale Kennels? They had one kitten left. If it's still there I'll buy it for my daughter, though . . ." He rumpled his hair, ". . . children can be funny. When her teddy went missing, no other would do. We just had to find it before we got any peace. It's strange no-one has seen Misty."

Misty! Silver! Surely old Mrs Cameron's cat must be grey? Gillian bit her lip, wanting to share this information with him. But what if she were wrong? And what if she were right?

The old woman was probably now greatly attached to her little Silver. She, too, was going to be hurt if she had to part with her new pet.

That evening Gillian called in at the corner shop near their offices and found out Mrs Cameron's address. Armed with one of the reward notices, she walked to the old lady's home, having to ring twice before the door was opened gingerly.

"Mrs Cameron?" she asked. "Remember me? I . . . er . . . I asked you about your little cat."

"Oh ay?" asked the old woman, refusing to open the door more than a foot.

"Have you seen this?" Gillian held out the notice.

"I can't see to read these days."

"Well . . . couldn't I come in and read it to you?"

After much hesitation the old woman invited her inside. Looking around quickly, however, Gillian could see no sign of the kitten.

"It's a notice about a reward for finding a Siamese kitten," she said. "It belongs to my boss's little girl. Haven't you seen it at all, Mrs Cameron?"

"Och no, nothing like that. I know what they are like . . . yellow sort of colour with brown ears. My cat is grey."

She pushed open the door of her kitchen where a fire burned brightly.

"I've got to keep the place warm for Silver," she said. "Here she is."

Beside the fire was a

Treasure-Chest

LITTLE old lady, so gentle and sweet,
  A bundle of fur — "Hello, Puss!"
— at your feet!
Your drowsy head nodding, a smile of
  delight.
Of what are your dreams in the cosy
  firelight?
Perhaps you are dreaming of long ago
  days,
Of satins and silks, and of time's leisured
  ways;
Of youth and its hopes and aspiring
  ideals,
A theme through the ages, that always
  appeals!
Little old lady, I wish that I knew,
So when you awaken, do tell me, please
  do!
I would not disturb such a beautiful
  sleep,
But if dreams were on view, how I'd value
  a peep!

— *Elizabeth Gozney.*

new and pretty cat basket where a small lilac-point Siamese kitten lay fast asleep on a soft knitted pink blanket. It was apparent to Gillian that nothing was too good for Silver.

She swallowed a small lump in her throat. It seemed that Silver might have made a big difference in Mrs Cameron's life.

"I knitted the blanket myself," she was saying. "And I bought her a good basket. The best. The best of food, too. She's a great wee cat. You should hear her purring when she comes to sit on my knee."

The old woman had taken the notice. "Did you want to read this to me?"

Gillian drew a deep breath.

"No, it doesn't matter," she said. "I'm sorry to have troubled you, Mrs Cameron. I only came because of . . . of Mandy. She's not very well at the moment after losing her kitten, but she'll get over it."

Mandy was going to get another kitten. She would soon forget Misty.

But what would Charles Bell say to her if he ever found out she had found Misty, and had kept quiet about it? His regard for her would plummet, and Gillian's heart plummeted at the thought.

Yet perhaps that was the best way to cure her of this growing attraction for the hard-working talented man she had come to admire so much. Surely she could not be in love with him, because apart from Mrs Bell, Mandy and Misty, she knew nothing about him?

She had never seen his semi-detached house on a nearby estate, and the only time he had referred to it was when he told her about the search for the kitten.

"We have plenty of neighbours," he had said. "My house is rather crowded in, but some day I'll design a new one."

THE office became very busy as their latest project — a large public building — began to get under way and Gillian had no opportunity to ask about the new kitten. All must be well now, she thought.

Charles Bell spent many hours away from the office on the building site, and it was during one of his absences that old Mrs Cameron arrived in Reception carrying Silver in a cat basket. Silver yowled piteously and the girl in Reception lost no time in contacting Gillian.

"I think it's someone for Mr Bell, Miss Tait," she said, "but he isn't in his office. Can you come down?"

The old lady was fighting tears when Gillian came to see her.

"It's no use," the old woman said. "I can't keep the wee cat. I looked up a book and I saw that it is a different colour of Siamese cat, so I know it belongs to that wee lass all right. And you said she was ill, so I can't keep her cat. I got Mr Bryson to show me where to find you, miss."

"Oh dear."

Gillian looked round helplessly. Mr Bell would not be back in the office for several hours.

"I'll leave her with you," the old woman told her, turning to go.

"No, it'll soon be my lunch hour, Mrs Cameron. I tell you what, we will go and take the kitten to Mandy. Maybe she won't want it now. She may have another one."

Mr Bell's home proved to be a small semi-detached house with a garden front and rear. The lady who came to the door was an older edition of himself.

"Mrs Bell?" Gillian asked.

"Yes, I'm Dorothy Bell." Her eyes fell on the cat basket. "Oh, goodness . . . Oh, you haven't found Misty at last, have you? Come in, please."

Gillian stood back to allow Mrs Cameron to go into the house in front of her, and Mrs Bell conducted them into a cosy living-room where a small fair-haired girl sat playing with her toys.

Another kitten, subtly different from Misty, played with a woollen ball, kicking it vigorously, but when Mrs Cameron put down the cat basket, the child seemed to leap into life.

"Misty!" she cried. "Oh, Grandma, it's Misty! she's come home! Won't Daddy be pleased?"

She had lifted out the little cat, ignoring the sharp claws which clung to her cardigan.

"Won't Daddy be pleased?" she repeated.

"And your mummy," Gillian said.

The dark eyes surveyed her solemnly though this time the child remained silent.

"Mandy lost her mother two years ago," Mrs Bell said quietly after a moment. "You're Miss Tait, aren't you? I recognise your voice from the telephone . . . it's quite distinctive . . . and Charles has talked about you."

"I'm sorry, I . . . I had no idea Mr Bell was widowed," Gillian was saying. She, too, recognised the clear bright voice, but the woman was much older than she had pictured.

Old Mrs Cameron was talking to the little girl.

"She's been on her holidays to my house, dear," she said. "I bought her a basket, and I made a blanket. I've brought that so that you can keep it. She's a lovely wee thing, isn't she? Full of mischief, though. You should see my best chair!"

▶ *over*

according to Custom

THE distribution of Maundy Money takes place each year on the Thursday before Good Friday. The Yeomen of the Guard accompany the Queen as she makes her way between the two rows of recipients who are equal in number to her age. The money itself is held in drawstring purses. It consists of specially minted silver coins and is in fact legal tender.

"Do you give holidays to cats?" Mandy was asking. "I didn't know cats had to go on holiday, like girls. Will you take Susie and give her a holiday? I like Susie, but she's not my cat. Misty is my cat."

Swiftly Mrs Bell bent down and picked up the other kitten, her eyes on the old woman.

"I . . . I don't suppose you would consider giving this wee one a home?" she asked hesitantly. "We got her as a replacement but there is no real substitute for a kitten you love."

"No, maybe not," Mrs Cameron agreed, "though it seems to be another nice wee thing."

She glanced uncertainly at Gillian.

"How about taking her for a holiday, to see how you get on?" Gillian suggested. She felt that she needed a holiday herself!

So Charles Bell was a widower! They had all assumed that Mrs Bell was his wife. He must have been shattered by her death which was no doubt why he was so withdrawn, though sometimes . . . sometimes he had shown interest in her.

But that changed nothing. When he had faced a family problem over Mandy's kitten, her sympathies had gone to old Mrs Cameron, and it was only the old woman's conscience which had resolved the matter happily for everyone.

Charles Bell's growing interest in her would soon vanish when he knew all the facts.

Quietly she accompanied old Mrs Cameron back home with Susie loudly protesting at being cooped up in a basket once again.

IT was difficult to explain her lack of loyalty to Charles Bell when she told him the whole story. His warm thanks for the return of the kitten had shown her that his regard was almost as warm as her own for him, but she had to tell him the truth.

"I knew it was lack of loyalty to you," she said unhappily, "but the old lady seemed to have so little. I had no right to make a decision like that . . . though I would have liked so much to have been the one to help you."

She blushed under his searching gaze.

"You didn't know I had lost my wife?" he asked. "I don't talk about it much, but there was a car accident. Mandy was with her in the back of the car, and she was saved, though we have to go easy with her until she begins to forget. She tends to cling to her possessions, as you saw with Misty, but we hope she'll grow out of it as she gets older."

"I . . . I see. I didn't know," Gillian said awkwardly.

"She needs someone young to talk to, now and again. Someone kind. For the most part, children have a great deal more than elderly people, and I think I might have chosen Mrs Cameron, too, given the same circumstances."

He turned to go back to his office. "By the way, my mother would like you to come to tea on Sunday. What do you say?"

Gillian's smile was bright with pleasure. "I'd love to come," she said simply. □

by
BEATRICE FIELD

PENNY was glad of the delay. Driving their neighbour, old Ted Simmons, to the church hall this morning had denied her the opportunity of passing on the sad news to her parents. Short though the delay was, it meant that her mum and dad could be happy for a little while longer. Still, she knew that she must tell them today — tell them, as gently as she could, that the wedding they were so looking forward to wasn't going to take place after all. She and Kenneth had parted in anger, with no plans to meet again.

She drove at a steady pace, following the usual route to church, the one she would have been taking in a fortnight's time. Picturing herself as

A HELPING HAND

she would have looked, sitting beside her father in the luxurious, roomy car, she remembered the whirl of happy excitement when she'd chosen her white gown.

For the moment, she allowed herself to feel the joy of stepping out at the lychgate and beginning the slow, eager steps that would have taken her up to the altar where Kenneth would be waiting; where, in joining hands, their future lives would have been bound together.

The moment ended. There would, after all, be no photographer clicking every happy smile into a permanent picture. No signing of the register declaring that they had become man and wife — just a pen-stroke here and there, crossing out bookings, cancelling every special item that had been ordered for that wonderfully-important day.

There was a lot of traffic this morning, more than usual, even on Saturdays. A fair number of people were transporting plants that they'd been so carefully growing, keen to place them in a good position for catching the judge's eye this afternoon.

Ted's blooms, his exhibits for today's show, were packed into the back of the car and their pleasant perfume enveloped the two of them.

"What's your favourite colour of flower?" Ted suddenly asked.

He must think I'm unusually quiet this morning, Penny thought. "Yellow," she answered. The bouquet she'd ordered was to have been of yellow and white roses.

They'd reached the church and Penny had to slow to a halt awaiting her turn behind the car in front, in the queue for the church hall. Leaning her arms on the steering wheel, she stared ahead and, in her mind, began to relive yesterday's row. Again she heard the angry words that had suddenly redirected her life along a sad, unknown way.

NO longer could she look forward to living in the little house that was to have been her future home. She had so looked forward to it. They had both loved it, small though it was, with its tiny plot that she'd planned to turn into a pretty garden. That was the point where anger had grown between them, and understanding had fallen apart.

"Naturally, we'll make a garden here," she'd insisted. "Who would dream of doing anything else?"

"I would, for one. We'll both be busy with our jobs and the housekeeping to do. When would we find time for gardening?" Kenneth had demanded with a sternness that had surprised her.

"You could use the time you'd otherwise spend in that garage you so badly want to build. 'A good-sized garage' you said; so there'd be no room left, no space for growing anything."

"And I can just see you wearing overalls all day and every day — I'd never see you except at breakfast and supper . . ."

"And when would I see you — a busy secretary, housewife and gardener as well?"

"You work in a garage all day long. Isn't that enough?"

"No, it isn't. I thought you knew me better than that by now. Haven't my ambitions got through to you yet, Penny? I'm not planning to remain

A Helping Hand

an employee all my life. I told you I aim to have my own business one day, and a garage of my own is vitally important."

In a softer voice, he'd pleaded, "You do understand, don't you? One day we'll have a bigger house, and a nice big garden, too."

"I only want the house we've got. I love it — our own little home where we'd be happy together." Her tears had begun to flow. "You've spoiled it already."

She'd rushed away from him, shouting that she'd see herself home. It's getting late, thank goodness. I can go straight up to bed without it looking odd, she murmured to herself.

She didn't want to talk tonight. Not to her parents, not to anyone. Still, she'd never gone up without saying goodnight, so she made herself stand still for a minute and breathe deeply, calming herself. Then she popped her head round the living-room door, where her parents were watching the late-night news.

"Good night, Mum, Dad," she said, as brightly as she could, and was closing the door again, when her father called her back.

"You all right for a spot of chauffeuring in the morning, Penny?"

"Well, yes . . ."

"Good. Ted's car has broken down again. Not too surprising, as he won't spend the maintenance time that old car of his needs. Too busy in that greenhouse of his. Still, we can't let him down, can we? It's his big day tomorrow. He won't be able to get his plants over there in the morning if we don't give him a lift."

"Yes, I'll take him. 'Course I will. Well, good night again."

She closed the door and made her trembling way upstairs, thankful to be alone to think, and to prepare herself for morning. She must go down appearing quite normal, because there'd be no time to tell her news at the breakfast table.

WHEN Ted's precious blooms had been unloaded and taken into the hall, he thanked Penny for bringing him and explained to her that he would be going to a nearby café to have his lunch.

"All right, Ted. I'll come this afternoon to take you back. Good luck. See you."

Now I must face it; get it all over, Penny thought. Heading for home she gripped the steering wheel tighter, trying to imagine how each of them would take the news.

I'm not sure about Dad, she thought. He likes Kenneth. He was glad about us becoming engaged.

She loved her father. His reaction, whichever way, would be important to her.

And Mum. She'll see it my way, surely. She loves a garden. She likes watching Ted working in his; she loves to tell people how he became so interested.

Penny remembered what had happened. It had been shortly before Ted's wife had died. A friend had taken Elsie a lovely bunch of blooms. "Aren't they gorgeous, Ted?" she'd whispered. "Isn't it sad that in a week or two they'll be withered and gone."

F   81

Soon after that, Ted was alone and, remembering his wife's words, he'd thought to himself, to keep beautiful blooms, we'll have to keep growing fresh ones. I'll do that for you, lass. From then onwards, he'd found contentment in keeping his promise, becoming more and more fascinated as time had progressed.

WHEN Penny reached home she found her mother bustling around the kitchen, wanting to get lunch on the table a little earlier than usual.

"Dad's just come in," she announced. "This morning he met up with an old friend, someone he hasn't seen for years. He and his wife are visiting this area. They've got a lovely car, Dad says, and they're calling to take us for a drive.

"I'm looking forward to it and Dad's pleased as Punch that he'll be able to have a long chat with old Charlie, as he calls his friend. We might call and have a nice tea somewhere. Will you be seeing Kenneth this afternoon, or is he tied up?"

"He's tied up," Penny responded, adding to herself disconsolately, tied up with his own selfish wants, and quite simply not prepared to budge an inch.

"He'll be more tied up in a fortnight's time." Her mother chuckled for a moment or two.

Penny wished fervently that everyone would stop being so bright and cheerful.

After lunch, she watched her parents leave, wondering when she would finally get her chance to tell them there'd been a sudden cancellation of her future happiness.

Dabbling her hands in soap suds, she imagined herself washing up at her own kitchen sink, looking out through the window where she'd already hung gay yellow curtains. There'd be the newly-planted garden . . .

She began to issue firm orders to herself. The caterers must be told, it isn't fair to delay any longer. They may get a replacement booking.

On her way to the telephone, she saw that her mother had left out one of the photograph albums, a big one that held many family pictures. Her grandparents were there, and others of their generation.

There were several wedding photographs and, as Penny settled down to look, she became more and more enthralled. She'd flipped through it before, of course, but never studied it intently, following the story of the generations.

The engagements, the weddings, the holidays and the high spots of the new century's young couples were all recorded there. Pictures of babies, crawling and toddling through the stages of childhood, delighted her. In the smiles of the young parents, she saw a lot of loving, understanding, give and take, unselfishness . . . Penny began to feel unsure of herself.

Eventually, turning the last page, she looked up from the faces of her forebears to the face of the clock and gasped with astonishment.

"Oh no! Ted will think I've let him down."

A Helping Hand

WHEN she met him, he was waving a certificate and a small cup at her. He'd won third prize for one of his entries. "The first time I've ever won anything," he told her with a broad grin, looking so overwhelmed that she rejoiced for him, in spite of her own heavy heart.

"I'm delighted for you, Ted."

"No more delighted than you'll be this time come a fortnight, eh?" The fun twinkled in his eyes.

Penny's uplifted moment was crushed. I must brace myself for this sort of thing, she warned herself, the aching inside her biting deeper. It'll happen again and again, until everyone knows . . .

They reached a quiet road, and Penny felt that she must share her sad secret with someone. Steadying her speed, she said, "I've a few places to call, cancellations to make, so we won't be home for a while. Do you mind, Ted?"

She stopped the car then and continued talking, telling her elderly companion all that was in her mind and in her heart. She told him every detail, the fragments she'd intended keeping to herself for ever, so glad was she to have a sympathetic listener.

Then she asked him again. "Will you mind if I stop here and there to make a cancellation?"

"No," he said thoughtfully. "No, I won't mind. Not if it's your wish, but I'll ask you one favour. Will you make one detour for me first? Won't take long."

"Yes, Ted. Of course I will."

★   ★   ★   ★

A YEAR and two weeks later, when Penny and Kenneth Turner awoke on the morning of their first wedding anniversary, they looked out from their bedroom window, down at the sun-filled plot that was their source of joy and pleasure. The garage stood proudly, it was big and roomy.

"I expect Ted'll come this morning. What a good friend he's been to us, Penny."

"All the hours of work he's put in here, for us, even when we've both been out at work. He's just as proud of that garage as we are, 'standing in its own garden' as he puts it."

Around each outer side of the building, Ted had secured a number of stout, broad shelves and along each one stood pots, tubs and containers — each one planted with flowers or a shrub of Penny's choice. As each colourful plant had its own particular type of soil or compost, there was a wonderful variety of growth.

The garage in a garden was a perfect copy of the one Ted had shown Penny on the afternoon he'd won his prize at the flower show — a small cup which he'd held for a year.

Now he had a prize which he treasured much more — it was the friendship and gratitude of the happy young couple whose marriage he'd helped to save, a prize that he could keep for ever. □

by BARBARA COWAN

AT HOME FOR HOGMANAY

TESS FULLERTON was hurt and angry, although only the white knuckles of her hand holding the telephone betrayed it. Her voice, as she sat at her desk in the chartered surveyors' office, was controlled and even.

"No, Stephen, I won't say definitely that I'll be at your sister's for New Year. But I'll let Angela know. Thanks for phoning."

She put the telephone down quietly, not surprised that her hand was shaking. She might be noted for her cool, even-tempered disposition, but Stephen Walker passing her up for another invitation at Christmas was something she found hard to swallow.

It had come as a shock to arrive at Angela's the other night and discover that Stephen, with whom she thought she had a growing understanding, had accepted a last-minute invitation from his boss for Christmas dinner. Even Angela, her long-time friend was flabbergasted, too.

" 'Atta girl, Tess! That's telling him!"

Eddy Rawlings leaned over his desk which faced hers. "I hope I hear there's a split in that friendship? Come to my party tomorrow . instead. Starts at eight prompt with dinner at my flat."

Tess looked coolly over at the rangy figure lolling on the opposite desk. Eddy was promoted to head of the department a few months ago, and she had to work closely with him. He'd become a disturbing influence in her life recently. She was never sure when he was merely teasing. But she wouldn't let him know it.

"What's the catch? Need help with the cooking?" she murmured.

"Well, I would enjoy that!" He nodded, smiling lazily over at her. Then he suddenly straightened up. "As a matter of fact, I'm getting a caterer in. So all you need to do is turn up as your own cautious, selfcontained, beautiful self! Think about it and ring me!"

"Thanks, I will!" Tess said, a little taken aback. She had worked in this office since she graduated six years ago, and it was the first time she had received a direct invitation from

Eddy Rawlings, although he did hint, especially since they had been working together.

But she was wary, not wanting to be thought of as another female conquest. Like everyone in the office she had, over the years, taken his phone calls from over-eager girlfriends, telling them he was at a meeting, or out of town. She doubted with her careful, precise nature that she truly appealed to Eddy. He liked his girls all bounce and frills.

"Come on — let that self-satisfied Stephen Walker see you have other strings to your bow," Eddy offered, watching her.

"Might at that!" She smiled noncommitally, and gathered up her handbag, and shopping.

It was now 5.30 p.m. on December 30, and four days holiday lay before her. Now all she wanted was to get home to her own special flat.

She felt secure there, and she could let the clever brittle shell that she surrounded herself with during working hours fall away. There the London professional was replaced by the home-loving side of her nature.

And she desperately wanted peace and quiet to try and untangle her feelings. In the last year Stephen had become a force in her life. She thought he saw her in the same light. But now she was not sure . . .

Yet was she blowing this one incident out of proportion as Stephen had said? True, she'd always spent Christmas with Angela even before she met him. But he had specially arranged to be there with her this year.

SHE entered the vestibule of the large apartment building, and smiled, accepting her mail from the caretaker in his little glass-walled office by the front door.

Like herself Jimmy Gordon was an exile Scot in London. He leaned forward confidentially.

"Doing anything for Hogmanay, Miss Fullerton?"

"Er . . . well, I haven't quite decided. I've got a couple of invitations, but I don't feel like accepting either of them," Tess answered truthfully.

"Mrs Gordon and I would be very happy if you came down to us for the bells, and to see in the New Year," he whispered, darting secretive glances to either side, although the foyer was deserted.

"Thank you, I feel very honoured," Tess murmured faintly, at this unexpected invitation.

"We have open house for a few hand-picked residents, so if you decide not to go out on your dates, come to us." Jimmy beamed at her.

"Oh yes, thanks!" She nodded and scooped up her mail, feeling touched by his kindness. Yet, the last thing she wanted was to bring in the New Year with total strangers. But if she didn't accept either Stephen or Eddy's invitation that was what would happen. She couldn't get out of it.

As she went up in the lift, she suddenly smiled at having three invitations. For years she had gone out to work, and come back each evening to various bed-sits, seldom being invited out. Then a year ago she achieved an ambition and moved into this exclusive block. It devoured a huge part of her salary, but she felt justified, since she spent so much time in her flat.

But then Stephen came on the scene . . .

She met him one evening through Angela, his sister. He ran her home, and her address impressed him. He started phoning, and she had gone out with him regularly since. It transformed her life.

Stephen knew so many interesting people who talked non-stop and never noticed if she didn't. He was ambitious — an up-and-coming man in the world of finance. Then he suggested they should think seriously of marriage. Tess liked that approach, as she always thought over carefully, every move in her life.

Then there was Eddy Rawlings . . .

One evening a couple of months ago he'd come round unexpectedly with some office work.

"You really have the nesting instinct!" he'd teased as he looked round her comfortable flat. His eye rested longingly on the chicken casserole she'd just taken from the oven.

Tess felt she had to invite him to share it. His eagerness to accept surprised her.

Then somehow he arrived to share several more of her suppers — always with an excuse for coming, like bringing a package she'd left on her desk, or some extra drawings or specifications she might need for interviewing a client next day.

He never needed persuading, even cheerfully admitted he tried to find excuses to come around at supper time.

Later as she washed up, she sighed, wondering about them both. Which of their New Year invitations should she accept? Since she'd come to London she spent Christmas with Angela, and the New Year holiday up in Scotland with her aunt, who had brought her up.

This year she and Stephen decided she would spend all the festive season holidays at Angela's with him.

So his pulling out on the arrangement had stunned her. She loved her career, but she had dreams, too, of someone special, someone she would share her life with — to whom she would always come first . . .

The phone ringing interrupted her thoughts.

I KNOW you'll be away gallivanting over the next few days, so I thought I would just wish you all the best now." Aunt Morag's comforting voice echoed on the end of the line from Glasgow.

Tess was delighted, and they chatted and exchanged news. Tess felt a sudden nostalgia for the cluttered tenement flat in the Langside district of Glasgow, where her retired aunt was born. She never changed anything in it.

Tess remarked wistfully just as they were about to ring off:

"Suppose you'll be seeing in the New Year with the neighbours upstairs as usual."

There was a little pause at the end of the line, before Aunt Morag replied.

"No, Tess. This year they've all had invitations to spend New Year with their married children. They'll all be away."

"Oh, no! Why didn't you say? You'll be on your own then!" Tess cried in horror. Aunt Morag had said nothing about this before.

"Someone will probably pop in." Her aunt was lightly dismissive.

"Yes, someone will — me!" Tess made a quick decision. "I'll jump in the car and be up with you in the morning. And that's final. Don't worry, this mild spell seems to be lasting and there's no frost or snow forecast," Tess rushed on, preventing her aunt arguing against her journey.

And it would be a life-saver. Tess could cancel all three invitations, with a clear conscience now.

"See you in the morning! Put a hot-water bottle in the bed!" she finished, suddenly quite lighthearted.

An hour later she stood by the phone, neat and practical for overnight driving in a tracksuit, with her case and various packages at her feet.

She braced herself and phoned Eddy first. His voice on an answering machine, telling her to state her name and message, made her smile. Somehow it was typical of him. Bang up to date with everything. Then she phoned Angela, explaining her change of plans.

"Hope it'll make our Stephen realise he can't take you for granted. And that career promotion isn't everything," Angela said grimly. She was angry at her brother's thoughtless behaviour towards Tess.

★   ★   ★   ★

As she locked her front door a little later, Tess gave a satisfied sigh, and turned for the lift. She was looking forward now to being back at Aunt Morag's on familiar ground for the New Year holiday.

Next thing, almost in slow motion, she found herself falling as her feet became entangled in one of her packages. She crashed down on her hands and knees, and for a moment remained on all fours, dazed.

Gingerly, she rolled over into a sitting position, and leaned against the jamb of the door, rubbing her left knee .

It was only when she started to walk, that she winced and knew her left knee was badly wrenched. Yet, since she could move it, she thought the numbness would soon wear off. Once she was on the motorway, out of the London traffic with no gear changes, it would improve from the rest, she assured herself.

Jimmy Gordon, the caretaker, immediately noticed she was limping, and she had to tell him of her silly accident.

"You're looking very pale, as if you've had a real shake," Jimmy said, frowning. "Maybe you should stay put."

"I couldn't disappoint my aunt now," Tess murmured, although she was wishing she had decided to set out tomorrow.

Once she was in the car heading out of London, her mind on driving, she felt soothed, like her old self — except for a dull ache in her knee.

After some hours driving, she pulled into a motorway service station for a coffee and a rest. As she opened the car door she rolled up the leg of her tracksuit and groaned at the swelling and bruising round her knee. Reluctantly she had to admit it was not getting better. And later, as she travelled on through the night, she felt the swelling becoming worse.

Then she saw the funny side. What would Stephen and Eddy think if they knew a painful knee had put them and their invitations completely out of her mind for hour after hour?

In Glasgow she came off the motorway and drove through the familiar streets towards Langside. She decided to go into the casualty department of the Victoria Infirmary. Commonsense told her now that she needed medical help.

according to Custom

FOR centuries inhabitants of Tissington in Derbyshire have been dressing the village's five wells — making up picture mosaics with leaves, flower petals, cones and other natural substances. The custom goes back to the time of the Black Death when the water in Tissington remained pure and people travelled from all over the district to draw water, thus avoiding the ravages of the plague.

IT was 8.30 a.m. when she limped in, and explained her plight to the blue-overalled assistant behind the glass screen. She took a seat to wait her turn for attention, while the domestic staff pushed floor polishers and mops industriously around, preparing for the coming day.

When her name was called, she limped into a cubicle.

The young doctor took a look at her knee, and immediately sent her for an X-ray.

Looking at the plates a little later, he smiled ruefully.

"You've cracked your patella — that's your knee cap!"

"Oh, no!" Tess gasped. "I'm due back in London by the fourth of January."

Then she watched in horror as the nurse wrapped a huge roll of cotton wool round her knee, then bandaged it into place. Her leg was about four times its ordinary size.

"Is all that necessary?" Tess wailed.

"Indeed it is!" the young doctor assured. "And for the next week we want you to stay off that leg as much as possible, and keep it raised on a couch or foot rest. The nurse will give you some exercises to do, so that your muscles don't get too weakened."

Tess listened in growing dismay as she was given instructions, and told to report back in a week's time. This was a nightmare. It would certainly teach her not to act on sudden impulse again. Suddenly she felt it was a judgment for running away, and not staying in London.

She stood up and looked down in distaste at her left leg bulging incongruously under the tracksuit trousers. Then it dawned on her — she simply could not drive like this.

The nurse nodded sympathetically.

"Better phone for a taxi!" she murmured, pressing a walking stick into Tess's hand.

The cheerful taxi driver drove her round to her parked car and transferred her luggage into his cab. When it drew up at the close of the stone-cleaned tenement, Tess saw her aunt standing up at the lounge window awaiting her arrival.

As she awkwardly got out of the taxi with her walking stick, and stiff leg, Tess almost heard Aunt Morag shriek. In moments she was downstairs, asking a torrent of questions. Tess held up her hand to stop the flow.

"Just a silly fall, as I was about to leave last night." She smiled. "And you might have me for a full week now through it."

"Ah well, every cloud has a silver lining!" Aunt Morag was briskly delighted at the prospect.

The taxi driver grinned at Tessa as Aunt Morag grabbed some of her parcels and trotted back upstairs calling:

"Don't move, I'll be back down to help you."

"Looks as if she's going to enjoy your bad leg!" the taxi driver quipped.

Tess nodded. "Yes, she'll smother me with care. Still, I might enjoy it for a week — it'll be a novelty."

Yet, she remembered it was Aunt Morag's over-concern which drove her to live and work in London. Aunt Morag always saw her as the forlorn little orphan, dazed from the unexpected deaths of her parents, and talked down to her as if she was one of her infant pupils. But what would she have done without her? This flat and Aunt Morag were rock-like security at that traumatic time.

Soon her aunt was helping her up the stairs to the first-floor flat. And it was only when she guided her into her old bedroom that Tess realised just how tired she was after driving through the night with a throbbing limb. Tess laughed at the pronounced lump in the middle of the bedclothes.

"You didn't forget my 'pig'!"

"It's been in since six this morning. And I refilled it with hot water just half an hour ago." Aunt Morag bustled around folding back the bedclothes. "And now get straight into bed. I'll bring you water to sponge your face and hands, then some breakfast."

"And while you're having it I'll arrange with someone in the block to go and pick up your car. If you'll just give me the keys . . ." Aunt Morag had everything organised.

Tess didn't argue — it would be no use. Aunt Morag was mistress in this house, and her will prevailed, just as it did when she was an infant mistress. And Tess did not want to argue.

Getting between the sheets with her old familiar stoneware hot-water bottle was a soothing comfort, even the *art nouveau* prints on the walls didn't annoy her as they used to.

IT was early afternoon when Tess opened her eyes sleepily. Aunt Morag's head was peeping round the door.

"Hope I didn't waken you!" She beamed, obviously delighted that Tess's eyes were open. "I've looked in a dozen times, but you were dead to the world. Your car's here by the way. It can stay parked outside — it'll be quite safe."

"Mmmmm! I feel quite rested." Tess struggled into a sitting position.

"The sofa in the lounge is made up, if you want to lie there in front of the fire. You'd be able to watch TV," Aunt Morag offered eagerly.

Holidays Ahead

EVERY spring as daylight lengthens
  And the sun peeps shyly through,
Thoughts all turn to days of leisure
  And of holidays soon due.

Shall it be the Scottish mountains,
  Or the little Channel Isles?
Maybe we should see Rome's fountains
  Or where Spanish sunshine smiles.

This way, that way, plotting, planning,
  Every year the problem grows.
Climbing mountains, wide lakes scanning,
  Aching legs and tender toes?

One thing though is oh so certain,
  Whether we go far or near,
Who we go with, that's the person
  Who will make the memory dear.
          — E. Horscroft.

"Good idea!" Tess threw back the bedclothes, knowing her aunt was desperate to talk. It was surprising that she had contained herself for so long.

"Here's the dressing-gown!" Aunt Morag handed her the old-fashioned tartan woollen garment, with the tasseled silk tie. It had belonged to her long-dead father, and came into its own in illness. When she was younger Tess thought it was part of the cure.

She lay on the couch, snugly enveloped in it, and ate the lunch Aunt Morag had prepared.

"Did you hear the phone this morning?" Aunt Morag asked excitedly, tucking a rug round Tess. "Rang about two hours ago. But I didn't want to wake you. It was a young man, Eddy Rawlings. Said your caretaker thought you were ill when you left last night, so he wanted to know if you had arrived safely."

She looked enquiringly at Tess.

"Oh, he's someone I've been working with in the office recently." Tess was off-hand. Aunt Morag had never married, but she was an inquisitive romantic.

"So he's not Stephen, then?" she queried.

"No!" Tess shook her head. She knew Aunt Morag was puzzled about Stephen's place in her life, and why she had changed plans about spending the New Year holiday with him.

"You must bring Stephen up to visit," Aunt Morag said a little reprovingly. She had extended the invitation several times.

"You never know, he might turn up to first-foot us," Tess said lightly, to divert her aunt from asking any more questions.

"This Eddy sounded very nice. Seemed to know all about me. Said you always speak well of me." Aunt Morag was pleased and flattered now. "He was very concerned when I told him how nasty your accident had turned out — more or less a broken leg, yet you drove all the way up here so that I wouldn't be alone at New Year!"

"Broken leg! Aunt Morag, it's not that bad!" Tess cried. "Provided I'm sensible, I'll be as right as rain within a month or so, the doctor said."

"Don't make light of it!" Aunt Morag said severely. "You looked quite desperately ill this morning when you got out of that taxi. Just a good job you're here so that I can take care of you."

Tess opened her mouth to answer, but closed it again. When Aunt Morag took charge, nothing would shake her.

★　　　★　　　★　　　★

Just before midnight, Tess lay on the sofa dozing, aware of Aunt Morag moving around the flat. She opened her eyes and smiled at the little wine table standing with a bottle of sherry, two long-stemmed sherry glasses, and a plate of shortbread and cut fruit cake, ready for the bells.

Aunt Morag bustled in, a duster in her hand.

"Like everything to have a shine for the New Year," she murmured, darting round the room giving all the surfaces a quick wipe.

Tess smiled and nodded. She knew Aunt Morag was keeping herself busy, so that she wouldn't dwell on too many old memories which always surfaced at this time of the year.

"Just three minutes to go!" Aunt Morag said, taking off her apron, and smoothing down her hair.

Tess saw the suspicion of tears shining in her eyes, but wisely avoided mentioning it. For all her bluster Aunt Morag was a private person.

The old grandfather clock in the corner started to toll out midnight, and in the distance they heard the church bells, and muffled cheers.

They hugged one another, just as the front door-bell pealed out, and they jumped apart in surprise.

"Gracious! Who can that be — at one minute into the New Year?" Aunt Morag said, then her face lit up. "Maybe it's your Stephen come to first-foot us!" And she ran to the front door.

Tess lay, ears straining. Then she heard indistinctly the deep tones of a man's voice, and Aunt Morag's happy shriek. She sounded as if she was being soundly embraced.

Tess knew it couldn't be Stephen. He was far too reserved for that. The door opened and her jaw fell as Eddy Rawlings' long figure entered the room, holding a beribboned sheaf of red roses in cellophane.

HAPPY New Year!" He handed the roses to her, then bent to kiss her.

He was the last person she expected, and that kiss had left her shaken.

"But . . . but . . . your party?" Tess gulped. It was the only thing she could think to say.

"Put it off!" He shrugged. "Wouldn't have enjoyed it when the principal guest was lying injured hundreds of miles away in Scotland. So I followed you. Just as well I did," he added. "You'll need someone to drive your car back."

"Look at my beautiful bouquet!" Aunt Morag said delightedly, cradling a large display of mixed flowers. "And you've got red roses, Tess! Six of them!" She looked at Eddy enquiringly.

"Yes, one for each month we've worked together," Eddy said,

Tess felt at a disadvantage, out of her depth, lying enveloped in this shabby old dressing-gown, without make-up. It was difficult to adopt the professional business-like stance which she used to distance herself from Eddy in the office.

"We'd better toast the New Year," Aunt Morag produced another glass quickly. She poured out the sherry, and handed them one each. "Red roses — no doubt what they mean. Maybe we'll be toasting your futures, too," she said roguishly, and Tess felt herself shrink in embarrassment, wondering how Eddy would deal with such a broad hint.

"I think that's a very good idea — in fact, the whole purpose of my coming!" He held his glass up towards Tess in a toast. "To a Happy New Year, and a happy new future which I hope you'll let me share — preferably for the rest of our lives."

Tess lifted her glass in return toast, suddenly feeling a quiet joy. And she knew she could stop running away from Eddy. He was the one who had put her first.

"We might give it a try!" she said, quietly cautious.

"Yes, till you are walking again — then we can see about an engagement ring." Eddy laughed. "I'm taking no chances. Stephen Walker must know once and for all he's lost, and I've won!"

"I'm glad!" Aunt Morag agreed. "Never met him, but I think I like you better!"

They all laughed, and Tess had the feeling that her future had just been decided for her — and it was a wonderful feeling! □

A S the grey roofs of Robton came into view, Danny Stewart braked
gently and finally brought the car to halt in an unsurfaced lay-by.
He smiled reminiscently as he looked around him.

Many's the time he had come running up here when he was a little
lad. For in those days this had been the entrance to the slate quarry
where his father had been foreman.

Danny had loved coming up here, so had always volunteered to be
message boy for Mum if there was any sudden emergency, or to run up
with Dad's dinner "piece" on the infrequent occasions when he forgot
it.

The slate quarry had been closed for
many years now — indeed, that
was the reason for the Stewarts
having moved away from Robton into
the city when Danny was only thirteen.

Dad had become a bus driver,
and Mum, Danny and his sister,
Margaret, had had to
attune themselves to city life.

That had been twelve years ago.
And what a lot of changes there had
been since then!

Mum and Dad were now "Nana" and
"Papa" to Margaret's bonnie, curly-haired twins
who had started school last year and spoke over the
telephone from Toronto in strong Canadian accents.

Dad had acquired his own taxi business and was thoroughly enjoying
life. Mum ran a local playgroup and Brownie pack and was busier than
she had ever been.

As for himself . . . ?

Danny looked down at the doctor's bag on the passenger seat and
gave a sigh of contentment. Dr Daniel Stewart.

He had been only seven years old when he had decided what he
wanted to do with his life. By that time he had had more experience of
hospitals than most folk have in a lifetime. It was all a blur to him now,
lost in the mists of childhood.

NO TIME
FOR ROMANCE

Operations and setbacks. Finally the skilful heart surgery that had given him the gift of a normal, active life. But it had filled him with a burning desire to help other folk in the same way.

Then, later, there had been another reason why he had wanted to prove himself . . .

Danny's lips tightened momentarily and his eyes hardened. Then, as

by ELSPETH RAE

though shaking off some unpleasant reflection, he suddenly shrugged his shoulders, started the engine, and put the car in gear.

Five minutes later he was drawing to a halt on the gravel driveway of Dr Grigor's sandstone villa.

★ ★ ★ ★

"I'll leave you with a thought," James Grigor said the next morning, grinning a little as he leaned out of the window of a car that was piled with suitcases and holiday-luggage.

"I'm going to be looking for a partner when we get back."

"And the first floor can easily be converted into a self-contained flat," his grey-haired wife added eagerly.

"So if you like Robton, and it likes you . . ." Dr Grigor rolled up the window, waved goodbye to his startled-looking locum and was off.

"I had no idea *that* was in his mind," Danny remarked to Isla Scott, Dr Grigor's very capable nurse/receptionist, as he went through the waiting-room to prepare for the morning surgery.

Isla smiled. "It's Mrs Grigor who's really behind it," she said. "She thinks the doctor's overworking. She's quite right, too.

"Would you consider it, Doctor Stewart?" she added hesitantly, as though afraid he might think she was being nosey.

"Oh, I don't think so," Danny told her. "I've become used to city-life with all its amenities. I'd miss the theatres and the libraries and the sports facilities now."

"Yes. I did, to begin with," Isla said. "But then there are such a lot of compensations. Being able to walk up on to the hills and hear nothing but the peewits' calling and to see the sheep roaming free. The scent of the pines. Fresh eggs from the farm."

Danny looked at the blonde-haired young woman with a twinkle of amusement in his grey eyes.

"You don't need to try to sell Robton to me, you know," he said. "I was brought up here."

"Yes, I know that, Doctor," Isla said, flushing a little. "I was only explaining how I felt when I had to leave London to come here and look after my mother. I loved it there, you see.

"I'd got a job in the hospital where I had trained," she went on, "and I had a circle of really good friends. I didn't know how I was going to settle down here. It all happened so suddenly.

"My mother and father had bought a cottage here when Dad retired. And within a year Mum was crippled with arthritis and Dad had died."

"I see. But you're happy enough now?" Danny asked, looking at the young woman sharply.

"Oh, yes." She smiled. "I love my work. It's only my friends I miss. There aren't many folk of my age-group in Robton. And those that are seem to be staid married couples."

"Ah, well," Danny said, returning her smile, before he strode on into his surgery, "I expect I'll soon be meeting a few old acquaintances. Though Dr Grigor said I'll probably have a quiet time since a lot of folk are away on their summer holidays."

"Did he now?" Isla said with a chuckle. "Did he really say that?" Danny looked out of his surgery door.

"Don't you agree, then?" he asked doubtfully.

Isla's brown eyes were dancing.

"Well, let me put it this way, Doctor," she said. "If Dr Grigor was at home, he would have a quiet time. What he forgets is that whenever he goes on holiday, his regulars are so panic-stricken, they begin to imagine all sorts of symptoms. It's happened four times since I've been here with four different locums."

"I don't mind a bit," Danny said cheerfully. "I came here for the experience after all. The more patients I see the better. And I hope you don't mind, Nurse Scott, but I'd like to do as much as I can myself. Injections; taking blood-pressure readings; and so on. Dr Grigor said that was normally your department."

"Of course, Doctor," Isla said pleasantly.

Danny watched the young woman approvingly as she began to open the waiting-room windows.

I bet she was a jolly good hospital nurse, he thought. Calm and kindly and very pleasant to look at. Then his reflections were interrupted by the "ping" of the doorbell. The first patient had arrived.

B Y the end of two weeks Danny was feeling comfortably at home in Robton. Patients waved to him as he passed by in his car. If he walked into a shop he was greeted by, "What can we do for you, Doctor?"

"Dr Grigor's going to be a wee bittie jealous when he comes back," Isla Scott had informed him with a smile, thus letting him know that he was not a downright failure with the patients anyway.

Mind you, he told himself, much of the credit for that state of affairs ought to go to Isla herself. For Dr Grigor certainly had a treasure in his nurse.

She was adept at calming panicky patients, cheering up folk who were depressed, and dealing firmly but politely with the troublesome ones. She had a sense of fun, too, that Danny really appreciated.

He had knocked over an ornament in the hall one evening, a little china chimney-sweep, whose leg came adrift in the accident. Having placed the pieces on the hall-table with a view to sticking them together some time, he promptly forgot all about them. A few days later he had walked into his morning surgery to find the poor fractured chimney-sweep sitting in the patient's chair!

To Danny's eyes, the town of Robton had changed very little in twelve years. Most of the businesses were owned by the same families that he remembered as a boy.

Only over the garage, the bakery and the fruit shop, the name *MacPherson*, once printed in such bold, black letters, had been erased. Mr Allan MacPherson who had owned all three had died six years before, so Danny had heard, and his widow still lived alone — their daughter was in America — in the big grey-stone house at the back of the town.

Whenever Danny passed the house, whether driving in his car, or walking, he automatically averted his eyes. Not that he had any need to, since the place was closed up and dead looking, Mrs MacPherson being away on holiday.

There seemed few of Danny's contemporaries left in the town — certainly none of the gang he had once played with. He met their parents, though, and had soon stored up a heap of local tit-bits of news that he knew his mother would really appreciate.

"What has really shocked me," he told Isla Scott one afternoon with a chuckle, "is to discover that folk I honestly believed were about seventy, when I was ten, are only in their fifties now!"

"A lot of them remember you, Doctor," Isla told him. "I've been hearing how you always wanted to be a doctor and worked tremendously hard at school. They're all so pleased that you succeeded."

"I know they are," Danny said in a quiet voice. "They're a fine bunch of people."

★   ★   ★   ★

By the end of his third week in Robton everything was going so well that Danny was quite unprepared for the cloud that suddenly appeared on his horizon on Friday evening.

He had just finished surgery when Isla Scott poked her head round the door. She had changed out of her uniform and was wearing a pink linen suit which showed off her prettiness to advantage.

"I have an invitation for you, Doctor Stewart," She smiled. "That is, if you're not busy tomorrow evening."

"No, I'm not," he said, waiting curiously for Isla to continue.

"It's from Mrs MacPherson up at Pine Villa," Isla went on, "She's just home from holiday and is having a few friends round for drinks. She wondered whether I would bring you along to join them. She knows my mother, you see . . ."

"Oh, I'm sorry!" Danny said abruptly, frowning down at the desk. "I'm afraid I can't. I've some notes to write up. I'd completely forgotten about them. Work must come first, I'm afraid."

"Of course, Doctor," Isla said shortly. "Good night, then."

She turned away, but not before Danny had seen her scarlet face and the hurt look in her eyes.

As the outside door closed behind the young woman it suddenly dawned on him that she had thought he had been rejecting her, and not Mrs MacPherson's invitation.

"Oh, no!" He groaned, thumping his fist on his desk in exasperation.

He jumped to his feet and ran through the waiting-room. But he was too late. Isla had gone. And he could hardly go running after her with his schoolboy explanations. She would think he was mad.

THAT evening Dr Stewart might have been seen walking by himself up the long brae behind the town. When he was halfway up, he sat down on the heathery verge and gazed down on Robton.

He could see the roof of Pine Villa through the trees that sheltered it on the west side. And suddenly he was eight years old again, holding his big sister Margaret's hand and running along with a crowd of other children to Katy MacPherson's to see the new puppies.

How excited he had been! Then as he had been about to follow the other children through the big, imposing gateway, Katy had thrust out her podgy, little arm.

"He's not allowed in!" she had cried shrilly.

"Why not?" twelve-year-old Margaret had asked indignantly.

" 'Cos he's from the Home, and my mum says he might have bad blood. She says his mother and father might have been thieves or murderers or anything! And I've *not* to play with him."

"Don't you dare say that about my brother!" Margaret had stormed and had pushed Katy so hard she had fallen down on her behind with a wail. Then she had begun to cry herself, as she had run back home, pulling Danny behind her.

The incident had upset Danny terribly. Now he realised that his early years of invalidism had probably made him more sensitive than a normal, healthy child. After all, he had always known that he had been born in a children's home and that his mum and dad — the only mum and dad he knew — had not "found him," that had been Mum's phrase, until he was three and in the local hospital.

Yet it had taken all Mum's loving wisdom to help him over the

▶ *over*

according to Custom

THE Scottish Border town of Selkirk was once famed for shoemaking, and the Souters, to give the townspeople their nickname, have a colourful history. One event that embodies this is the Common Riding festivities which take place in June. Then the Souters ride the boundaries of the town and enact the ceremony of casting the flag in commemoration of the men who fell at the Battle of Flodden Field in 1513.

experience at the MacPherson's. He could still remember her telling him gently that it was true that they didn't know who his first mum was.

What they did know was that this first mum had loved hm very much, and had been very sad to give him up, because she had left him on the step of the Home in a little basket with piles of lovely little knitted clothes. And that she had done this so that a second mum and dad and big sister would be able to look after him properly and love him in her place.

Mum could be fiery, too, though. To begin with she had wanted to rush up to Pine Villa and tell Mrs MacPherson just what she thought of her. In the end, however, she had decided that the best thing would be for none of them to ever step through the gate of Pine Villa again.

Margaret, Danny's staunch protector and ally, had grimly agreed to this rule, and had played with Katy no more. Danny had recovered from his initial shock and grief, but for many years afterwards had been troubled by a nightmare in which a hand had suddenly barred his way and a giant voice had yelled, "Thief! Murderer!"

And in his childish way, when he had wakened, he had vowed, time and time again, *I'll show those MacPhersons! I'll become the most famous doctor in the world!*

Now, as Danny rose slowly and started back down the hill, he sighed deeply. Here was Mrs MacPherson causing trouble for him again. And because of her he had hurt the feelings of Isla Scott.

And for some reason whenever he thought of Isla's hurt brown eyes a cruel little hand squeezed his heart more and more painfully.

D ANNY was sitting in the garden on Sunday morning after church reading the paper.

When he heard the scrunch of feet on the gravel he thought it was Mrs Dickie who had been coming in to cook for him every day. Then he heard a polite cough and looked up to see Isla Scott standing, poker-faced by his side.

There had been no surgery on Saturday, so he had not seen the young woman since she had left on Friday evening. Now he felt his face burning as he tried desperately to think of what to say to her.

But it was Isla who spoke first.

"I'm sorry to disturb you, Doctor," she said coolly, "but Mrs MacPherson asked me to call in and say she'd be very pleased if you could have tea with her this afternoon — if you're not otherwise engaged."

"Oh, no!" Danny dropped his head in his hands with a groan. When he looked up, Isla was still there, looking down at him in some concern.

"Is there something wrong, Doctor?" she asked hesitantly. "Can I help?"

Suddenly Danny knew that a girl with such warm eyes would listen to him with understanding. That she would think him neither stupid nor childish.

"Are you in a rush?" he asked her. "Or can you spare a few minutes?"

For answer Isla sat down silently on the bench beside him.

Danny took a deep breath then launched into an explanation of his behaviour on Friday evening.

Isla's eyes were full of compassion when he had finished.

"I understand how you feel," she said quietly. "But has it occurred to you that Mrs MacPherson might be wanting to apologise?"

"Oh, no!" Danny said. "That would be more embarrassing than anything! . . . Yet I suppose I'll really have to go," he finished uneasily. "Otherwise it will look so rude."

"Would it help if I came with you?" Isla asked after a moment.

"It certainly would!" Danny said very positively.

"Then I'll be round here at five to four, Doctor," Isla promised.

Just after four o'clock Danny and Isla sat down in Mrs MacPherson's sunny sitting-room.

"My dear," Mrs MacPherson called gaily to Isla as she wheeled the trolley in, "Isn't it lovely? I couldn't believe it when I heard who was acting locum for Dr Grigor! Dr Stewart here used to come to the house with his sister and their friends to play with my Katy. And it only seems like yesterday to me."

★　　　★　　　★　　　★

"She's completely forgotten what she said about you, Doctor," Isla said quietly as they left Pine Villa an hour later and started down the hill.

"I know," Danny said. "I could see she wasn't pretending. She honestly thinks I was one of Katy's playmates."

"It's quite frightening," Isla said sadly, "how people can hurt other folk without even realising it. Like running over them in the dark."

How nice it was to have someone to talk to like this, Danny thought suddenly. For years his studies had come first, and he had never had time for romance. Besides he had never met anyone . . .

But here was a girl who seemed to be reading his thoughts.

"Isla," he said suddenly.

The young woman turned to look up at him, her cheeks like roses, her eyes glowing.

"Yes?"

"I think I might accept Dr Grigor's offer."

"Really?" There was no mistaking her joy now.

Danny's heart gave a great lurch.

"And since there aren't any patients around, I think you might call me Danny," he added.

"Danny," she said, as though to try it out, and gave the little giggle that he loved.

"I think Mrs MacPherson's made up for everything now," Danny said slowly.

Isla said nothing, just looked up at him nodding slowly. But her eyes told him that she understood what he meant. For hadn't Mrs MacPherson brought them together?

"I'm so glad I came back," Danny said, taking her hand. □

The Only Girl For Him

"THAT'S it finished for another month, thank goodness." Craig Crawford shuffled the papers into a tidy pile and stood up and stretched. "I'm glad you started up as a farm secretary, Aileen."

He smiled down at the dark-haired, brown-eyed girl who was still sitting at the table. "You've been a life-saver for me! I'm a farmer, not an accountant."

"You wouldn't last long as a farmer if you didn't take money into account." Aileen returned his smile and snapped shut her brief-case. She stood up, small and petite against his six feet two inches.

"What about coming with me to the ceilidh the Young Farmers are organising tonight?" she asked, changing the subject. "All the crowd will be there. It's sure to be great fun. And there will be a disco afterwards. What do you say?"

Craig stuck his hands into his trouser pockets and shifted his weight from one foot to the other.

"Well, I don't think I can go . . ." He hesitated, "Your crowd don't exactly welcome an old chap like me."

"Old!" exclaimed Aileen. "You're only twenty-eight! Just because you bury yourself playing with that collection of old farm machinery instead of socialising more."

by SHONA JAFFREY

103

Craig tried to think of an appropriate excuse but before he could speak Aileen continued.

"We've been working hard all afternoon. Surely we deserve some time off? Let's go out and enjoy ourselves. It will do you good, you old man, you!"

Craig sighed inwardly but agreed. "OK, then, What time shall we meet?"

Later, when Aileen had left, Craig went into the farmhouse kitchen where his mother, Meg, was preparing the evening meal. His grandfather, Duncan Baird, was sitting at the kitchen table reading his paper.

They both looked up as Craig entered.

"Is Aileen away ?" Meg enquired.

"Yes, but we're going to a ceilidh in the village tonight."

"What a good idea." His mother's tone was enthusiastic. "Aileen's a nice girl," she commented, then added thoughtfully, "She never fails to come in to have a chat with me when she's here to do the books.

"She makes all her own clothes, you know, and she's a good cook. She's got a good head on her shoulders for all she's only twenty."

"A bit too full of herself sometimes," Duncan muttered from behind his paper, but his daughter turned on him sharply.

"A show of character never goes amiss," she said. "There's no doubt she's got initiative."

Craig took his seat at the table and allowed the comments to float around him. He knew that his mother looked on every girl he took out as a prospective daughter-in-law and that Aileen Kennedy met with her whole-hearted approval.

"Mum." Craig laughed. "You're too transparent for words! I'm only taking the girl to a ceilidh, not to the altar!"

"It has been known that one thing leads to another." Meg had the grace to chuckle. "After all, at your great age of twenty-eight a wife might be a good idea!"

Craig noted that twice in a very short time he had been made aware of his age. He reflected upon the inferences that arose in his mind.

THAT night at the ceilidh, Craig found himself sitting in a corner observing the proceedings rather than being part of them. With his mother's views fresh in his mind he had decided to try to get to know Aileen better.

In the past he had tried to talk to her but her inability to listen had always defeated his good intentions. Tonight there was no difference and Craig retreated into silence.

Aileen didn't even notice. She had no difficulty in talking to him. Her words washed over him, swept away on waves of noise drummed out by the disco which had succeeded the earlier folk music. There was no need for him to respond.

Craig allowed his thoughts to wander and he wondered when he could decently make a move to go home. Eventually he shouted at Aileen over the noise of the music.

The Only Girl For Him

"Do you mind if we leave now? I have an early start in the morning even although it is Sunday?"

The unsocial hours required by farming never failed to provide a fool-proof excuse for a strategic retreat.

They walked along the darkened streets to the edge of the village. Aileen prattled on about all the people that had been there. Craig tried to feel less judgmental. After all, he reasoned, Aileen was only twenty, pretty and attractive and full of feminine foibles.

"I'm so glad we went to the disco," she enthused, "I really did enjoy it." She hung on to his arm. "There's another one next week. Let's go to that. It's on Saturday, too, so you're bound to be free. Shall we meet at the same time?"

This time Craig had his answer ready.

"No, Aileen, I'm sorry, I can't go next Saturday," he replied firmly, but she looked so disappointed that he added by way of explanation, "Grandfather and I are going to a farm sale over by West Lothian. There are one or two carts included in the catalogue and we want to see how old they are."

"Fancy spending your Saturday gazing at old carts!" Aileen laughed. "What on earth can you do with an old cart? Anyway," she continued without waiting for his reply, "there's hardly enough room in the byre for another piece of machinery. So, what are you going to do with all that junk?"

Craig tried as best as he could to keep the exasperation and irritation out of his voice.

"I think you know what I'm going to do," he said. "I'm collecting agricultural machinery which is of historical interest. One day perhaps I'll be able to open a museum. I find it fascinating to study these machines and find out how farm workers used to manage in what were meant to be the good old days.

"Those were the days of horse-drawn machinery — reapers, ploughs, threshing machines and so on. The ingenuity of the designs and the workmanship is amazing. But it is the way of life they represent I find so absorbing." Craig stopped, aware that Aileen was bored by his enthusiasm.

"Sorry," he apologised, "I know I get carried away sometimes when I start on that subject."

"Well, I think you'd be better to put your money into buying a new car to replace that old banger you've got now. I know you can afford it, too!" Aileen's smile and teasing tone of voice took the sting out of her words.

▶ *p108*

Until the bridge was opened the most direct route from Inverness to the Black Isle was via the ferry between North and South Kessock. This impressive structure spanning the Beauly Firth has changed all that, opening a speedy new link to Dingwall and the far North of Scotland.

KESSOCK BRIDGE, Inverness-shire : J CAMPBELL KERR

"Och, change your mind, Craig. Take me to the disco next Saturday," she coaxed.

"Sorry, Aileen." Craig was surprised to find himself unmoved by her pleas and to realise that he had no desire either to go to the disco or to be in her company.

He looked at her upturned, pretty face illuminated by the light of the moon.

"Sorry, Aileen," he repeated, "I can't go."

"Oh, well," she resigned herself to his refusal, then added, "but we will go again soon, won't we?"

THE following Saturday, Duncan Baird and Craig set off for the farm sale. It was a beautiful summer day and as Craig's old banger carried them steadily along they enjoyed the display all round them.

The countryside was in full bloom with ranges of lush greens interspersed with brilliant splashes of colourful wild flowers.

Craig always enjoyed his grandfather's company. Duncan Baird had spent a long life in farming and there was little he didn't know of the problems that arose or how to find solutions to many of them. Craig acknowledged that he had learnt everything from his grandfather and he was grateful for the training he had received.

As Aileen Kennedy had confirmed in her review of the financial position of the farm, both Craig and Duncan knew the methods they applied to the arable and the animal management of their land were successful. In addition to their working partnership Craig and Duncan shared an interest in agricultural change — the methods, the people and the history.

"Do you remember the first farm sale you took me to, G.F.?" Craig had substituted the initials for "grandfather" for as long as he could remember.

"Ay, I do that!" Duncan's eyes twinkled at the memory. "You'd be about five years old . . . just a wee laddie. Your dad died when you were two and after that your mum brought you back to the farm so that we could all live together. You were a born farmer even then."

He paused and sucked at the empty pipe he stuck into his mouth.

"But where was the first sale?" Craig prompted.

"It was on a farm near Forfar," Duncan remembered. "But of course, in those days I was buying machinery I could use on the farm . . . and as cheaply as possible! There was no spare cash to purchase old, useless bundles of scrap metal! Everything had to pay its way."

Craig squeezed the car into the parking space in the field adjoining the steading where the sale was being held. They had reached their destination.

"Let's go and look at the carts first before too many people arrive," Craig suggested.

They found the carts easily enough in a shed which backed on to the main steading. Several people were there examining them in a desultory fashion.

"They're in very good condition," Craig commented to Duncan in a low voice. "Even the bolts on the side-boards seem to be free of rust. And the wheel hubs have been greased. I bet we could use them on the farm right now."

Craig walked admiringly round the carts.

"Ay and we'd have to buy a pair of Clydesdales to pull them!" Duncan chuckled, then added feelingly, "Remember that you get a couple of hours less in your bed if you're working with a horse. It isn't much fun having to get up early on a dark, freezing winter morning to feed your horse before you can begin the work at all! Mind you, horses are warmer to the touch than tractors."

"Hey, G.F.," Craig called urgently. "Come and see what's over here! Now, this really is a find!"

"What is it?" Duncan followed him. "Och, that's a reaper-binder. Not in such good condition as the carts. They must have had it stuck away in here for years. It looks much like the one I worked in the 1930s . . . with three horses."

Both men walked slowly round the machine fingering the sprung cast-iron seat and the wooden flails.

"There's still a roll of bindertwine left in the box. That was used for tying up the sheaves, wasn't it?" Craig sounded excited. "It looks as if the whole machine hasn't been moved since it was last used. It's marvellous. I'd like to buy that. I wonder how much it will fetch?"

"Depends on how many people want it," Duncan replied shrewdly.

"Well, *I* want it," declared Craig. "We can let the carts go this time and just go for this."

As he spoke he became aware of a figure standing nearby. He glanced across and observed a lady almost as tall as himself, dressed in blue. Her face was shaded in the dim light of the shed but he caught an aura of calmness surrounding her.

She seemed to acknowledge his stare with a half smile before giving her attention to the notebook she held in her hand.

Craig moved closer to Duncan and together they discussed how much they would bid for the reaper when the auction began. Craig felt excited by the prospect of not only owning a piece of equipment of that antiquity but of working on it in order to restore it to its former function.

As he waited for the auction to begin he wondered about the successive men who had sat on the hard cast-iron seat throughout hot harvest days. How they must have watched the jerky rhythm of the machine as the flails gathered the golden grain into sheaves.

"The auction is about to begin, lad." Duncan's elbow nudged Craig back into the present. "You do the bidding."

CRAIG knew the auctioneer and he concentrated on observing the pattern of the bidding as item after item was brought forward and put under the hammer. The old, disused machinery was left until the end so Craig and Duncan had a long wait.

As time passed Craig noticed that the "lady in blue," as he had dubbed her in his mind, who had also been examining the reaper, bought a number of items.

Craig noticed that the blue dress she was wearing was matched by the colour of her eyes. Her fair, long hair framed her oval, fine-boned features. Her expression was relaxed although she was intent on the bidding.

She projected a calmness yet a warmth that made Craig feel he would like to talk to her. Suddenly she looked in his direction and their eyes met. Craig felt himself flush and he immediately lowered his gaze.

When he stole another glance at her she had turned her attention again to the auctioneer.

Craig wondered how old she was and guessed that she must be in her mid-thirties. Again Craig felt Duncan's elbow in his ribs.

"The reaper's next. Are you ready?"

"Yes, of course." Craig concentrated on the auctioneer.

At the beginning the bidding for the reaper was lively but gradually bidders dropped out until only Craig and one other bidder were left in contention. The "lady in blue" was Craig's opponent.

Craig reached the sum that he and Duncan had agreed would be their limit but she bid higher. Craig looked at his grandfather and raised an eyebrow questioningly.

Duncan nodded, indicating a further bid. Craig bid. The "lady in blue" bid higher. Craig felt anger rising in him. He was very keen to have the reaper and the competition was only increasing his anxiety to possess it.

He looked again at Duncan who indicated he could make one more bid. Craig did so and the "lady in blue" topped it. Craig had lost. The reaper was knocked down. Craig was furious.

"What on earth can she possibly want with something like that?" he snapped to his grandfather, making no attempt to lower his voice. "Anyway, she's paid well over the odds for it!"

"I expect that was going to happen no matter which of us actually got the reaper in the end." A quiet voice said evenly at his side.

Craig swung round to find the "lady in blue" beside him. She had a sympathetic smile on her face. "I'm sorry if you are disappointed," she added gently.

"It really doesn't matter," Craig returned coldly, and turned on his heel leaving his grandfather to make amends.

▶ *p112*

Glamis Castle has been owned by the Lyon family since the 14th century — the present day building dating from the 17th century. In more recent times the impressive baronial castle was the childhood home of the Queen Mother and it was there in 1930 that her younger child, Princess Margaret, was born.

GLAMIS CASTLE, Angus : J CAMPBELL KERR

Craig wandered round the rest of the steading and gradually regained his composure. He knew he had acted childishly and he felt guilty and shame-faced. He quickened his pace in an effort to try to see the woman again before she left. Then he could apologise and he might also discover her name.

He rounded a corner sharply and nearly knocked over his grandfather.

"Hey, laddie, look where you are going!" Duncan stopped abruptly. "And where did you disappear to? You left me in a pretty uncomfortable position, too!"

"Yes, I know, G.F. It was stupid of me but I was really disappointed about that reaper," Craig said. He glanced about hopefully.

"If you're looking for the lady in question, she's gone home," Duncan told him. "She and I had a long chat. She's a very interesting lady and very knowledgeable, too." He sucked his pipe thoughtfully.

"Her name is Laura Ramsay. She bought the reaper for a museum in the West but she's in this part of the world for a while doing some kind of research . . . something like that."

"Laura Ramsay," Craig repeated. The name seemed to fit the person, he thought.

He wished he had acted in a more courteous way towards her although her purchase of the reaper still rankled. He now had to return home empty-handed.

"OH, good," Meg Crawford greeted her father and her son when they appeared in the kitchen doorway. "You aren't as late as I had expected."

She busied herself in lifting dishes out of the oven. "By the way, Craig, Aileen phoned. She

Timely Reunion

ANXIOUS to meet my loved one,
home again
From a business trip across the world.
Due in at dawn now, first plane of the
day.
I'm driving on an empty motorway.

Gleaming wings slice through clouds on
high,
Familiar colours on the tail I spy.
Oh, how romantic, soon we'll meet once
more!
Can't wait to greet the man that I adore.

Ahead, the plane descends behind a hill
Towards the airport — I've got ten miles
still!
Traffic increases in the outer city rush.
Takes time to park the car — how I must
rush.

He must be past Customs and
Immigration!
I'm running now with the dread
realisation —
He's right on time, I'm twenty minutes
late.
He's come twelve thousand miles — I
fifty-eight!

— *Karin Stanley.*

wanted to speak to you. I said you'd phone her back when you came in."

"Oh, Mum," Craig protested. "I really have nothing to say to her."

"Go on," Meg returned firmly. "Think yourself lucky that a girl like Aileen takes an interest in you."

Reluctantly Craig disappeared into the hall to use the telephone there.

When he reappeared Meg inquired, "Well, are you going then?"

"Oh, Aileen told you she wanted me to take her to the Young Farmer's dance tonight, did she?" Craig responded angrily. "Well, I'm not taking her, neither tonight nor any other night. OK?"

"We met a nice girl at the sale today," Duncan interrupted tactfully. "Only Craig didn't much like her either!"

"G.F.!" Craig exploded but then had the grace to laugh as he caught the teasing gleam in his grandfather's eye.

It was five days later that Craig saw an unfamiliar car parked in the yard. Curious, he walked quickly into the kitchen, but before he could speak he saw his grandfather shaking his head, his finger to his lips.

Craig shut his mouth abruptly and closed the door quietly behind him. He saw a tape recorder sitting on the table flanked by his grandfather and by Laura Ramsay. He sank into a chair to listen and observe.

"Tell me what happened when your grandfather was hired at the Lammas Fair," Laura Ramsay said to Duncan who began to tell of people and happenings and customs in a way that had always fascinated Craig. At last Duncan stopped speaking.

"I'm fair dried out, lassie," he said. "I think we'll be the better of a cup of tea."

"That was really interesting," Craig enthused. "I thought I'd heard all your stories, G.F., but you were talking about some people I hadn't heard you mention before."

"Ah, that was because you've never asked me such good questions as Laura," Duncan replied.

"I'm Laura Ramsay and I expect you're Craig." Laura had switched off the tape recorder and turned to smile at Craig.

She put out her hand and Craig held it, warm and strong, in his. Their eyes met and Craig felt enveloped in a glowing sensation. It was a whole new feeling of well-being.

"Yes, you're right," he replied. There was short pause then he plunged on, "I want to apologise to you for my behaviour at the sale. I'm sorry. It was childish but I was so keen to buy the reaper."

"That's quite all right," Laura reassured him, "I don't really like auctions because someone is always disappointed. The reaper was a find. It isn't often something as interesting as that turns up. Perhaps you'd like to come to see it again, when I've been able to find transport to get it moved."

"Are you having difficulties?" Craig asked.

"Yes, it isn't proving as easy as I had thought," Laura replied.

"Laura is researching into the history of farming in Scotland," Duncan interrupted, impatient to inform Craig. "She's going to have

H

several sessions about the old days with me, aren't you, Laura?"

"Yes, please." She smiled gently at him. "You're a mine of information."

She turned to explain. "I'm collecting as much detail as possible from elderly people who can remember what happened, not only in their own day but also in their parents and grandparents' time. The best way to collect the information is to ask them to talk and then I can record everything." She gazed at the tape recorder.

"I believe you have quite a collection of old agricultural machinery and other pieces of interest," she went on. "I'd love to see them."

"Would you?" Craig sprang to his feet. "I'll show you now if you like."

"And I'll tell Meg that Laura will be staying for supper," Duncan announced as Craig escorted Laura from the room.

★   ★   ★   ★

Craig had never known days to pass so quickly. Every day he met Laura at the farm. She spent her time visiting elderly people in the district and recording their memories and reminiscences.

There was so much for Craig to talk to her about. Laura listened so attentively. She understood so well. Craig felt the day was empty until they met.

One evening he watched and listened as Laura and Duncan discussed the old toll houses and how the toll roads were maintained, or not, according to the different attitudes that prevailed. Laura's expression was animated and lively yet the peace she always exuded — and that Craig found so appealing — was evident.

Craig felt happy just to be in her company. Suddenly, the realisation dawned on him.

I love her, he thought. I love her.

With equal clarity a second revelation followed. I'm too young to ask her to marry me. How could she seriously consider marrying someone so much younger? To her I must be a boy. She would want someone older.

The feeling of sadness almost overwhelmed Craig. He was imprisoned by feeling of helplessness. There was nothing he could about it.

These feelings persisted and Craig grew quiet, almost subdued. Even his mother remarked.

"Goodness, Craig, whatever is the matter with you? I can hardly get a word out of you these days!"

Laura didn't say anything but Craig knew she was aware that all was not well. On several occasions he caught her looking at him with a puzzled expression. He would like to have explained to her how he felt but somehow he found that too difficult.

Craig had offered to provide transport to convey the reaper to its new home and one Saturday he and Laura set off to collect it. It was a beautiful day. The sun was hot and high in a blue sky. Craig felt the cloud of sadness lift from him.

Suddenly it was enough to enjoy the present — to feel Laura close beside him, her bare arm brushing against his. He listened to her soft voice as intently as he heard the words she spoke and he felt relaxed and happy.

They supervised the transportation of the reaper and eventually it was manoeuvred into position in the museum.

Laura leaned against the machine and turned towards Craig. She was wearing the same blue dress she had worn when Craig had first seen her. Craig felt his heart race. She was so beautiful.

"You know, Craig," Laura began thoughtfully, "Duncan has been such a help to me. I'm very grateful to him and count him as a real friend."

"I think he looks on you as a friend, too," Craig replied, then added, "I suppose that's rather funny seeing he is such an old chap."

"Age has nothing to do with it." Laura said gently, and looked straight at Craig. "The only thing that matters is how people feel about each other. Loving someone has nothing to do with age."

There was silence as Craig allowed her words to crystallise is his mind. Gradually he realised that Laura must care for him, too. He leaned forward and gently kissed her lips.

Hand in hand they walked away. At the door Craig paused. He looked back at the reaper and inwardly acknowledged his thanks for the part it had played in bringing such happiness to him. □

according to Custom

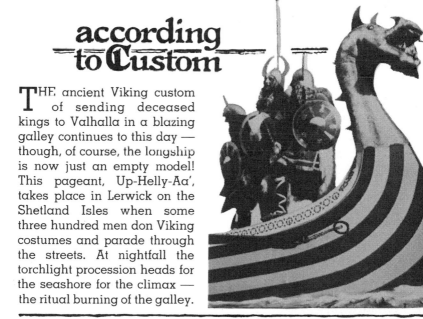

THE ancient Viking custom of sending deceased kings to Valhalla in a blazing galley continues to this day — though, of course, the longship is now just an empty model! This pageant, Up-Helly-Aa', takes place in Lerwick on the Shetland Isles when some three hundred men don Viking costumes and parade through the streets. At nightfall the torchlight procession heads for the seashore for the climax — the ritual burning of the galley.

To Make You Mine

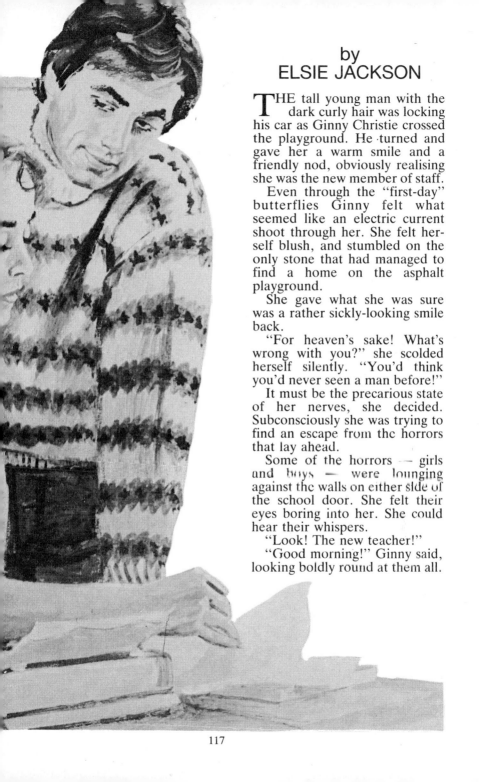

by
ELSIE JACKSON

THE tall young man with the dark curly hair was locking his car as Ginny Christie crossed the playground. He turned and gave her a warm smile and a friendly nod, obviously realising she was the new member of staff.

Even through the "first-day" butterflies Ginny felt what seemed like an electric current shoot through her. She felt herself blush, and stumbled on the only stone that had managed to find a home on the asphalt playground.

She gave what she was sure was a rather sickly-looking smile back.

"For heaven's sake! What's wrong with you?" she scolded herself silently. "You'd think you'd never seen a man before!"

It must be the precarious state of her nerves, she decided. Subconsciously she was trying to find an escape from the horrors that lay ahead.

Some of the horrors — girls and boys — were lounging against the walls on either side of the school door. She felt their eyes boring into her. She could hear their whispers.

"Look! The new teacher!"

"Good morning!" Ginny said, looking boldly round at them all.

That was one of the things they had taught her at training college. You had to take the initiative.

But she had lost her audience already. The eyes had swivelled beyond her. Sugar smiles had appeared on the girls' faces, comradely ones on the boys.

"Good morning, sir! Good morning, Mr Caldwell! Can I carry your case, sir?"

"Good morning, you lot! No thank you, Karen. I think I can just about stagger along to the staff room. It's not heavy — I haven't been paid yet."

There was a roar of appreciation, then Ginny became aware that the door was being held open for her. She looked up into a pair of warm brown eyes and felt her heart somersaulting absurdly again.

"I'm Keith Caldwell. English Department. I take it you're Ginny Christie."

"How do you do?" Ginny said in a weak voice.

"All the better for seeing you arrive this morning," Keith said cheerfully. "We've been short of a teacher in the English Department for two months and we've all had to lose free periods."

Ginny's heart slowed down. This was the reason for that warm, devastating smile, then!

"Some of the pupils look a bit . . . outrageous," she ventured, as they reached the first floor and turned left. "That rainbow-coloured hair. And all those funny clothes."

"Yes." Keith grinned. "That's our head's policy. Indulge their fads and they won't feel repressed and rebellious."

"Does it work?" Ginny asked.

"You'll soon find out," Keith told her. "You'll be teaching them. That's another of our head's theories. New young faces, still wet from training college, so to speak, work wonders on difficult pupils."

They had reached a door marked *Women's Staff Room.*

"Don't worry," Keith said with that smile again. "Any problems, you come straight to me. I'll be only too pleased to help."

As he strode off an amused voice behind Ginny remarked, "Ah! I see you've met our heart-throb already."

And she turned to find a pleasant-looking, grey-haired woman.

"I'm Lynne Wilson, your Head of Department," she said, as she ushered Ginny into the staff room. "No doubt Keith's told you we're very glad to see you."

M OST of the women staff had arrived and were drinking coffee, and Ginny was duly introduced and invited to join them. The two youngest teachers, Shona McKay, who taught French, and Mary Smith, the blonde maths teacher, took Ginny under their wing.

"Well? What do you think of Gorse Comprehensive?" Mary asked Ginny at the morning break.

"It hasn't been as bad as I thought." Ginny smiled. "I've had 2G and 3B and they were pretty well behaved on the whole."

"Och, I'm sure you'll manage fine," Shona said encouragingly.

"I hope so," said Ginny, adding "and Keith Caldwell said he'd help if I came up against any problems." To her horror she felt herself blushing.

"Oh, yes," Mary said in a resigned voice, and exchanged a look with Shona, who gave a funny, little laugh.

When Mary and Shona had gone off to the scullery to wash out their cups, Mrs Wilson slipped into the chair beside Ginny.

"Don't get any wrong ideas about our Keith," she said to Ginny in a low voice. "He's the pleasantest young man you could meet. The trouble is he went out with both Mary and Shona at different times. And they both fell for him rather badly.

"However, it seems each time his mother stepped in, and that was that. She's terribly possessive apparently. A widow with her last remaining son at home. You know the set-up."

"Poor Keith," Ginny said after a moment. "It's not much a look-out for him."

"No. Nor for any girl that becomes attached to him," Mrs Wilson said. And there was no mistaking the note of warning in her voice.

But with the best will in the world sometimes people cannot control the tugging in their heart-strings.

Ginny did her best, but after six weeks she had to admit to herself that her

Reflections In A Puddle

I AM encouraged when I see
  Reflections in a puddle.
For where they are there must be light
  To dissipate the muddle.

Reflected in its watery base
  The clouds go scudding by,
And hope will speed them on their way
  Below the azure sky.

So look with sunny countenance,
  As you a friend would greet,
Upon reflection, what you see
  Could make your day complete.

If only you would realise,
  Though life's a puddle true,
That what is mirrored in its depths,
  Is largely up to you.

Reflect on this — the pattering rain,
  Assisted by the light,
If smiled upon will bring you cheer,
  Imagine your delight.
            — Mignon H. Cook.

working days were now high-lighted by meetings, conversations, even glimpses of Keith Caldwell.

At staff meetings it was bliss to sit beside him and laugh at the humorous comments he whispered in asides to her. Three times he had stopped at the bus stop and given her a lift home, insisting that he was really going over in her direction that afternoon. But had he been, a hopeful, treacherous little voice in her head whispered?

Could he be interested in her? Could something so miraculous happen?

"Of course, if he did ask me out, I wouldn't go," she informed herself in the bedroom mirror one bright June evening. "I'm certainly not going to become involved with a man who's so attached to home."

Then when, the following afternoon, he stopped her in the corridor to ask if she would like to go to the theatre to see the latest Alan Ayckbourn comedy, she said:

"Oh, I'd love that! He's one of my favourite playwrights."

HAD the theatre outing been a failure she might have been saved. But it turned out to be one of the happiest evenings she had ever spent. Apart from the embarrassment of meeting Mrs Wilson and her husband on the stairs as they came down from the theatre restaurant.

Keith and she had so many interests in common, it was almost unbelievable. Had there been the remotest possibility of their ever having a life together it would have been an idyllic one. But of course there wasn't.

Already Keith was beginning to introduce his mother into the conversation. It was like a distant grumble of thunder whenever he said:

"My mother thinks . . ." or "My mother was just saying . . ."

"My mother always liked us to be independent," Ginny said a shade desperately. "That's why we all found jobs away from home. Mind you, we always phone my parents at least once a week, my two sisters and myself. Jo is in Stirling and Alison's in Aberdeen."

"Oh, I'm afraid I was a bit too fond of home comforts to move out," Keith said easily. "Mother's a marvellous cook."

Ginny almost groaned aloud.

She was slipping deeper and deeper in love. By now the staff knew, and she received pitying glances from Shona and Mary whenever Keith appeared at the staff room door to talk to her.

Mrs Wilson made no comment, but she always spoke to Ginny in a gentle tone, as though she were an invalid.

The pupils had heard of the romance, too. But they took a more optimistic view of the outcome.

After a particularly happy evening with Keith just walking round the city park, Ginny phoned her sister Alison in desperation.

"I don't know what to do," she shouted down a bad line. "I'm heading for disaster. Like a lemming."

"Like a what, Ginny?"

"A lemming. I'm a lemming!"

In the room across the hall, Ginny's landlady looked at her husband.

"There now!" she whispered. "I told you I'd heard her talking to herself. Now she's saying she's a lemon!"

"It's that teaching," her husband muttered. "A terrible nerve-racking job."

It became even more nerve-racking in the third week of June. The Inspectors were coming . . .

To Make You Mine

"Hoora! Hoora!" Nancy Henderson, the science teacher, sang to the tune of "The Campbells Are Coming," and did a jig up and down the staff room.

"Why did you ever join this mad profession?" Mrs Wilson asked Ginny.

"Oh, I'm glad I did!" Ginny said fervently. Otherwise I would never have met Keith, she added silently. Then felt that everyone in the room was reading her mind.

ON the eve of the Inspectors' visit Keith gave Ginny a lift home. They both had a pile of exercise books to correct for the inspection.

"Dump them on the back seat beside mine, love," Keith told her as he started the engine.

As she went to leave the car at her lodgings he leaned over and kissed her on the cheek. It was the first time he had ever done that and her heart raced like mad. She lifted her books and went into the house in a daze of happiness.

The world was a wonderful place, there was no doubt about it. Even the toasted cheese she made herself for tea tasted like smoked salmon. Then as Ginny reluctantly banished her daydreams and settled down to her corrections, her expression changed.

For the top dozen books on her pile were not hers, but Keith's. She must have lifted them from the car along with her own. And if she didn't take them to him straightaway, he was going to be in trouble.

Ginny was halfway to the bus stop before the implications of what she was about to do struck her. She was not just on her way to see Keith. She was about to meet his mother, too.

And since Mrs Caldwell probably did not yet know of her existence, there was bound to be some sort of repercussion. She tried not to think of what this might be. But during the twenty minutes of her bus journey, she found herself envisaging it over and over again.

Keith saying gently, "I'm sorry, love. But I don't see any future for us. My mother depends on me, you see. She has to come first. Of course we'll always be friends . . ."

Selfish woman! Ginny raged as she hurried along the avenue and up the Caldwells' trim drive.

The front garden was a picture with roses and forget-me-nots. This is why she won't let go of her son, Ginny thought bitterly. She needs him to look after the place. No thought of his happiness.

Perhaps she rang the doorbell rather loudly. At any rate the small, bright-eyed woman who presently answered it looked distinctly alarmed.

"Yes?" she asked, eyeing Ginny apprehensively.

"Keith left some books . . . I mean I picked up some of Keith's exercise books," Ginny stammered, proffering the books.

"Oh, my! He's just gone back to school to look for them. He thought he'd forgotten them," Mrs Caldwell said. Then she giggled.

"You are Mrs Caldwell?" Ginny said, wondering if she had chanced on an amiable aunt by mistake.

"Yes, I am," the little woman said. "And you . . . you're not Ginny? . . . Ginny Christie? . . . You are! Oh, come in, my dear! Come in! I've been dying to meet you. And this is ideal. When Keith's out of the way."

So she can warn me off, wondered Ginny, feeling bewildered. This woman was so pleasant and friendly. Could she really be such a dragon underneath?

L ET'S go into the kitchen and have a cup of tea," Mrs Caldwell said happily. "I can't tell you how glad I am you've come. I've kept asking Keith to bring you here, but he was afraid he'd frighten you off, he said, showing he was serious so soon."

She stopped in the middle of infusing the tea. "Gosh! Maybe I shouldn't be telling you this," she said doubtfully.

"Oh, please! Go on," Ginny urged her.

"Well, I'd almost given up hope of ever having a third daughter-in-law." She chuckled as she laid out cups and saucers and a plate of biscuits.

"Though, mind you, he is only twenty-six. But both his brothers were married at his age. And I do want to see him settled, too. He just never seemed to meet 'Miss Right.' He went out with girls, of course. But they always did all the chasing, if you know what I mean. I think he's quite attractive, isn't he?" she asked Ginny uncertainly.

"Very," Ginny said.

"Yes. Well, these young women used to chase after him. And he'd go out with them. He's a very soft-hearted lad, you know. Then they would get serious, and he would be in such a state wondering how he could break off the friendship.

" 'You must just tell them,' I would say. 'You have to be cruel to be kind.' And he would say he hadn't the heart. Of course he did manage it in the end. I never asked him how, though."

Just as well, thought Ginny, hiding her smile in her teacup.

"Anyway," Mrs Caldwell went on happily. "The first day he set eyes on you, my dear, I knew! This is her, I said! He had that moony, dreamy look that both his brothers had. And he spends about half an hour preening himself in the bathroom before he leaves for school in the morning . . .

"You do care for him?" she suddenly asked, her maternal instinct coming to the fore. "I know it's selfish. But I'd hate him to be hurt. And he would be, if . . ."

"Mrs Caldwell," Ginny said softly, "I love Keith with all my heart."

"Well!" exclaimed an indignant voice behind her. "Fancy telling a chap's mother that, before you say it to him."

Ginny gripped the two hands that had fallen on her shoulders.

"And I pinched your exercise books, too, darling," she confessed.

"Honestly!" Keith sighed. "I don't know what sort of a wife you're going to make at all . . . Do you, Mother?"

But Mrs Caldwell had tactfully slipped out to pick a few roses for her future daughter-in-law. □

IT was late autumn and the sun was beginning to cosy down behind far-off Ben·Lomond when Ella Robertson padded her way slowly on her daily walk from Dunblane to her cottage on the road to the nearby village of Doune.

Ella, a well-preserved, neatly-turned-out 60-year-old — and a widow for several years — tended to find time hanging heavily on her hands these days. She read a little and watched television rather more than she wanted to. She had never been an enthusiastic knitter or sewer. But she did enjoy her daily expedition into Dunblane.

Apart from buying her essential groceries, there was a baker's shop

by SANDY REID

Ella's Big Surprise!

123

which boasted a wee tearoom and Ella could usually rely on meeting up with somebody she knew with whom to share a cup of tea.

Earlier this afternoon Ella had been lucky. She had bumped into an old friend and they had shared a pot of tea and enjoyed two of the café's well-known fruit scones and raspberry jam before saying their hearty cheerios to each other.

Ella went off to finish her shopping in a much lighter frame of mind. Once home she quickly made some scrambled egg and toast. Then she tidied up and was just settling down to watch the six o'clock news when the doorbell rang. She jumped up, startled. She didn't usually have visitors in the evening and wondered who it could be.

Slightly apprehensively, she opened the door to find Willie Bruce, the local policeman, standing there.

"Good grief," she cried. "What brings you here after six?"

Willie Bruce would call in the mornings if he was going past and he was good for a few minutes' good-natured banter. Ella would ask about his wife's health and how his daughter was enjoying being a nurse in that big hospital in Dundee. However, this time his face was serious and he shuffled his feet nervously.

"I'm afraid I've a bit of bad news for you, Mrs Robertson," he said as she led the way into the sitting-room.

"Bad news?"

"It's your sister . . . in Leeds."

"You don't mean Chrissie." Ella sat down.

"Ay, I'm afraid I do." Willie cleared his throat before going on. "I don't rightly know how to tell you."

"Well, out with it, man. As long as she's no' —"

"I'm sorry but — she is," Willie stammered.

"Oh, no," Ella said.

Willie shifted from one foot to the other.

"But how would you know a thing like that?" Ella asked.

"Well, a lawyer in Leeds has been on the phone to the station and I was asked to come down and tell you."

"Poor Chrissie." Ella sighed. "But she would have died in her bed, no doubt. I never knew a woman fonder o' her bed than Chrissie."

"You're wrong for once," Willie said. "She was out for her shopping and she dropped dead in the street."

"Poor Chrissie. But it wouldn't be the weight of the messages Chrissie was carrying that would cause it," Ella said. "For an egg would keep her half a week."

"You don't seem as heart-broken as I was expecting," the bobby said reprovingly.

"I confess I'm not ready to faint at your feet," Ella admitted. "But you see, Chrissie was the first of the family and I was the last. She was a bossy besom all her days and to tell the truth, I never got on with her. And, though I'm sorry to hear your news, I haven't seen Chrissie for years."

"Don't forget she's your sister," reminded the bobby. "And the lawyer in Leeds expects you down there tomorrow to see to things."

"Me?" Ella said. "Why me? What on earth can I possibly do?"

"Is there anybody else?"

Ella thought hard. "I don't suppose there is," she admitted. "But Leeds is an awful long way from here. Can't I just tell the lawyer to get on with things?"

"Wait a minute." Willie Bruce held up a hand. "There's bound to be things he'll want to talk to you about. You being the only sister, and the chief mourner."

"Well, it's an awful nuisance," grumbled Ella.

"It's hardly your sister's fault!" Willie put in.

"I suppose you're right." She paused, thoughtful for a moment. "How does anybody get to Leeds from here?"

"By train, of course."

"And how do I get in touch with the lawyer?" Ella went on.

"I've got all the details." The policeman patted his notebook in his tunic pocket. "It'll be too late to travel tonight," he went on. "You'll get a bus into Glasgow tomorrow morning. There's a train for Leeds at ten o'clock."

He tore a page from the notebook. "Here's the lawyer's name and address. Would you like me to phone him in the morning and tell him you're on your way and you'll be calling on him in the afternoon?"

"Ay, I suppose so," Ella said. "You seem to have set your heart on me going to Leeds so you may as well finish what you've started."

"You're a right hard case," the bobby said. "Little wonder so many folk fight shy of you."

THE following afternoon Ella got out of the station at Leeds, handed a taxi driver a piece of paper on which she'd scribbled the lawyer's address.

"Take me there," she said.

Five minutes later she was being shown into the lawyer's office. A tall, silver-haired, military-looking man greeted her.

"I'm McGregor," he said. "You'll be Mrs Robertson."

"That I am," Ella said, taking the chair opposite his desk that he offered her.

"It was very good of you to come down all this way," Mr McGregor said kindly.

"I agree with you," Ella replied firmly. "Couldn't you have just made the necessary funeral arrangements yourself?"

"Yes," Mr McGregor said. "In fact, I have taken the liberty of arranging everything in advance of your coming. Subject to your approval, of course. However, there are one or two papers I'd like you to sign. Your sister's estate and that sort of thing."

"What do you mean estate?" Ella said.

"Well, your sister wasn't a wealthy woman." The lawyer paused and looked across the desk. "But she was — how would you put it . . . a careful woman."

Ella snorted. "That she certainly was. She wouldn't give you the price of a bus ticket if she could help it."

The lawyer went on as if he hadn't heard Ella's remark.

"I can't give you an accurate estimate of her estate. Her house is small — it'll have to be sold and it's impossible to say how much it will fetch. There's her furniture, too, and she has a few pounds in the bank. Give or take a few hundred I'd reckon the estate will bring in well . . . several thousand pounds."

"Did you say several thousand?" Ella said.

"I did, and it's all yours, or will be one day."

For the first time in her life Ella fainted — but she took care to faint into the big chair beside the lawyer's desk.

Two minutes later she came round to find Mr McGregor on his knees beside her and holding her hand.

"I've never done that before," Ella stammered, as she regained her composure. "That was right stupid of me."

"My fault entirely," Mr McGregor said. "This whole thing has obviously been a great shock to you. I should have been a great deal more considerate in my approach."

"I confess my heart's not made of granite, whatever some folk might think. But it's not shock that did that to me." Ella was once more sitting upright in the chair. "It's hunger. I was up early this

Storm In A Teacup

STORM in a teacup — what a stir,
   If things could be just as they were
Before someone's unthinking chatter,
With sugary asides caused a clatter.
Some useless observations which
Brought tension up to fever pitch,
Where something added to the pot
Produced a brew now scalding hot.

If one could silently take tea
Without the constant repartée,
Of snide remarks and hurtful splashes,
Which whip up into cruel lashes.
A storm that often seems to rise
From some teatable paradise,
And leaves a scene of desolation
Around the cup of consolation.

Come! Change the cloth, refill the cup,
And with forgiveness drink it up;
With Orange Pekoe, Earl Grey, China,
And lesser brews, there's nothing finer
To foster goodwill, and procure
A friendship that will long endure.
So let all teacup storms subside
And lose their force in friendship's tide.
      — Mignon Cook.

morning and only had time for a cup of tea before catching my bus to Glasgow. I've been in buses and trains and taxis all day and I haven't had a bite to eat. I'm starving, man."

"Well," Mr McGregor said. "I can't do much to help you get over your shock but I can do something about your hunger. May I suggest I take you for a meal right away? It's a bit early for dinner but I know a small café near here. I usually have my lunch there and I'm pretty sure they can come up with something at this hour of the day. If that's all right with you."

"It certainly is," Ella said, now completely recovered. "But a café? . . . I'd like something better than beans on toast. I canna stand beans."

"I'm sure they'll manage something better," Mr McGregor put in. "By the way, have you arranged for a hotel for yourself for tonight?"

"I have not." Ella looked at him. "I thought I would just stay at Chrissie's place. She'll have a spare bed, I suppose."

"I'm sure she has," the lawyer said. "But I don't think that would be a very good idea."

"And why not?"

"Well, it'll be cold and a dreary place for you to spend the night — under the circumstances."

"Would a hotel not be very expensive?" Ella queried.

"I'll fix a nice hotel for you and arrange for the bill to be sent to me," the lawyer said. "It'll come out of the estate."

Ella brightened a little. "You're not such a bad sort of man after all," she admitted.

IN the café Ella examined the menu carefully.

"I don't know what some of those funny names mean," she said, "so I'll just stick to fish and chips. Though heaven knows where they'll get their fish in this part of the world!"

"Grimsby or Hull, I expect," said Mr McGregor.

"Is that far from here?"

"Not that far." Mr McGregor smiled. "I think it'll be fresh enough for you."

"I'll take your word for it," Ella said. "By the way," she went on, "I've been listening to your voice. What part of the world do you come from?"

McGregor smiled. "Not that far from your own home. Actually, I was born and brought up on a farm halfway between Dunblane and Crieff. When I was a bairn my mother used to take me to the shops at Crieff and sometimes to Dunblane. Depending on the mood she was in."

"Imagine that," Ella said. "You've just about lost all your accent."

"Well, I haven't lived there for more than forty years. When I passed my law exams I got a job in Leeds and here I've stayed."

"You're a strange man, right enough," Ella said. "Have you never had any ambition?"

"Ambition for what?" The lawyer looked at her keenly.

"Why, to come home, like any other self-respecting Scots laddie."

McGregor laughed out loud. "You're a bit of a card, Mrs Robertson, so you are. You don't believe in beating about the bush, do you?"

"I've never seen any point in not telling the truth. It saves a lot of valuable time for one thing."

McGregor smiled. "I must say it's been a very refreshing experience to meet someone like you. Very refreshing, indeed."

They finished their meal and Mr McGregor took Ella to her hotel.

"You've had a tiring day," he said after she'd signed in and had been given her key. "No doubt you'll be wanting an early night."

"That I am," Ella said. "I'll no' need rocking tonight. And if I can't sleep I can always think about Chrissie and all that money she's left me.

"It's not much use to me," she went on, "but I've a son in Aberdeen and he has two bairns. I'm sure he can be doing with a pound or two."

"I wish you happy dreams," said Mr McGregor as he saw her to the hotel lift.

"You can be sure of that," Ella replied.

"Now remember," the lawyer added, "you're to come down to my office tomorrow, after breakfast. I've a wheen o' papers for you to sign."

"A wheen?" said Ella. "You're beginning to sound more like a Scotsman by the minute!"

McGregor smiled wryly.

"It's catching," he admitted. "It's catching."

Next day, after they had signed the papers Mr McGregor gathered everything together. "Now, there's just one thing more, Mrs Robertson." He paused. "You accused me yesterday . . . of not having any ambition."

"I didn't mean to accuse you," Ella said. "I just meant I was surprised."

"Would it surprise you to learn," the lawyer went on, "that I'm

according to Custom

THE traditional cry "Oyez! Oyez! Oyez!" can still be heard annually though it's hundreds of years since town criers did the rounds relaying the news to a largely illiterate population. Today, Hastings is the venue for the National Town Criers Championship when competitors come from far and wide to ring their bells and make their proclamations.

The cry "Oyez!" comes from the French and means to give ear, something the onlookers in Hastings are glad to do to the ceremonially dressed town criers.

Reproduced by kind permission of Hastings Tourism and Leisure Dept.

128

retiring in a month's time and that I've been considering what I'm going to do?"

"Ay, you surprise me," said Ella. "You seem a bit young to retire."

"I'm sixty-six years of age," McGregor said proudly.

"You don't say." Ella's face was expressionless. "I'd have put you down at nearer the seventy mark."

McGregor's face fell.

Ella leaned forward and slapped his arm.

"Ach, I was only joking. You're a fine figure of a man."

McGregor's face lit up again.

"I said yesterday that you were a card, Mrs Robertson."

"So you did," Ella said. "A joker. You get it? A joker."

McGregor smiled. "Yes, I get it." He paused. "I was about to say, about my retiral, that I was wondering if I should think about going back to Scotland."

"Don't think about it."

"Why not?" said McGregor.

"Don't think about it. Just go!" Ella put in forcefully.

McGregor smiled. "You've nearly talked me into it. What's Dunblane like these days?"

"Same as ever," Ella replied.

"Is the golf course still there?"

"Ay, it's still there and it seems to be quite a grand place now, judging by the number of motor cars that seem to be about the place."

"And the cathedral?" said McGregor.

"Of course it's still there. What would you expect?"

"I'd have to look for a house to live in," the lawyer went on. "Are there many houses for sale about the place?"

"A wheen," Ella said. "In fact, there's a very posh bungalow just down the road from me and they tell me it's coming on the market any day now. An English professor at Stirling University and his wife live there but I'm told they're going back to England."

"Is it the kind of place that would suit me?" McGregor looked at her.

"Oh, you'd have to go and see it for yourself," Ella replied. "You wouldn't want to take the word of an old fish-wife like me."

"I'm sure I could do a lot worse than take your word for it!" He laughed. "But I'll take a run up north and have a look at it for myself, though it sounds as if it might be just right for me."

"There's only one snag." Ella raised an eyebrow.

"What's that?"

"You'd have me as a near neighbour."

McGregor smiled. "You know, Mrs Robertson, I think I could stand that."

"There's something else," Ella went on. "A house like that would cost a bonnie penny. I'll tell you what," she went on, "if you're short of a bob or two, what with all Chrissie's money I could lend you a few quid."

McGregor smiled. "I think I'll manage," he said. "But it's a very neighbourly thought, so it is. Very neighbourly and very typical." □

ɪ

WHERE HER HEART LAY

A NGELA RAINTON
stared at her
husband, unable to
believe her ears.

"Move! Leave Calaby!
Simon, we couldn't!"

"Look, love, if
Paterson's close I shall be
out of work. There's work
for me in Yorkshire!"

"You don't know about
Paterson's! Not for
certain, and there will be
other work here. There
must be. Simon — this is
home."

Simon Rainton stood
up, leaving his breakfast
half eaten. His kind
brown eyes were worried
as he looked at his young
wife. He took her face
between his hands and
pressed a gentle kiss on
her unresponsive lips.

"We'll see, love," he said softly. "We'll see."

After Simon had left for work, Angela tidied the tiny cottage they had made their home when they married two years earlier. But somehow the tasks she so enjoyed doing had lost their savour and again and again her eyes went to the surrounding hills.

Angela had been brought up in Calaby. Her mother had died when she was only small, but her father, Bill Maclean, had been both parents in one.

by
MARY SHEPHERD

He had passed on to his small daughter his passionate love of the outdoors. Long before she could climb herself he had carried her up the hills, putting her down to play on the soft turf, teaching her to swim in a small, sheltered burn.

As she grew older Bill had taught her about the dangers of the hills, insisting that young as she was she carried her own small haversack with her own small waterproofs and a supply of chocolate and nuts inside.

Although the hills around Calaby were not dangerous, Bill knew that if Angela's love of climbing developed she would need every scrap of valuable knowledge she could gain.

Angela though, met and fell in love with Simon Rainton when she was only nineteen and settled happily in her beloved Calaby. But her father's training held her in good stead and she never went up the hills without her "emergency equipment."

It was always kept ready in her haversack, and several times when the mists had come down or she had gone further than she had intended, Anglea had been grateful to her father for his training.

Now, thinking of leaving her hills, of leaving this corner of Scotland that was home, Angela's heart was heavy, and she did what she had always done. She took her troubles to the peace and quiet of her beloved slopes.

Pausing only to slip on a cardigan Angela thrust her feet into her strong walking boots and headed for her goal.

★   ★   ★   ★

She had been climbing about an hour when she realised she had done the unforgivable! She had come to the mountains *without* her haversack.

For a while she hesitated, almost hearing her father urging her to return. But she looked up at the stretches of green sward and saw where the April sun glinted on the tarn.

All was soft and gentle and she went on, sure that these hills she loved would not hurt her — not when she needed them so! Needed their peace and the reassurance of familiar places.

Angela went on for about another hour, sometimes negotiating a narrow path, sometimes pulling herself up a patch of scree, but it was dry and the young girl knew every stone, every bush.

Soon she was at her favourite spot. Not at the top but high enough for her to view the valleys below, to see the old church where she had married Simon, and in the distance the big red building that housed the engineering firm which employed her husband.

Angela remembered her words at the breakfast table, but deep in her heart she knew that Paterson's could close. Rumours had been going round the town for a long time, and what other work was there for Simon round here. He loved his job, loved the challenge of designing new pieces of equipment. But Yorkshire!

Angela thought about some of the books she had read. Old stories of mining towns, of railways cutting through the countryside, of long rows of identical terraced houses!

Angela had not travelled far from Calaby. She had never wanted to. Now she thought about Simon and remembered the quiet gravity in his voice when he had talked about being unemployed.

Again and again her eyes rested on the stone tower of the small church, and the words of the wedding service echoed in her mind. *Cleave thee only unto him, as long as ye both shall live!*

Was she going to fail at this first test? Suddenly her throat went dry and she leaned over, filling her cupped hands at the clear brook beside her. Then, her thirst quenched, she lay back and stared up at the clouds above her.

She tried to imagine life without Simon, and could not. He was part of her now, and she knew that if the future they had planned had to take a different course, she had to accept it — not only accept but welcome it and make it work for both of them.

Angela tried to remember more about Yorkshire, and drifted into memories of television programmes. There was the Herriot country, in the lovely Dales, there were the Yorkshire Moors, she had seen pictures of them, wild and sweeping. Angela's eyes closed.

WHEN she woke the mists had come down. She could no longer see the church or familiar landmarks. Angela had no reason to fear, though.

She had been in hill mists before, and although the chill damp struck cold through her cardigan, and she cast more than a fleeting thought to the woolly jumper in her haversack, she knew she would be back down in the valley before any harm could come to her.

She didn't take the path over the scree. That would be too dangerous in the poor light. Slowly, carefully, she went round the hill to come down on the safer, gentler slope at the other side. From there she could easily make her way home.

By the time she was passing the mountain rescue hut at the far end of town she was really cold, and knowing there was always a stove and emergency supplies inside she went in.

Clem Atkins, an elderly member of the team who usually hung about to relay messages, looked up in surprise.

"Hello there, Angy! Not seen that husband of yours?"

"Simon? No, he's at work!"

"No, he isn't! He came home early for some reason. Guessed where you'd gone, then when the mist came down he panicked. Said you hadn't your gear and he set off to find you."

Angela's eyes opened wide.

"But, Clem! Simon can't go up the hill! Not in this. He isn't an experienced climber and he doesn't know the paths!"

By now the old man, too, was looking worried.

"He seemed confident, said he'd make his way round to the other side. You always used that path."

"Not in this weather. Clem, is there any spare clothing here I can borrow? I must go after him!"

"Nay, lassie, you can't! Not on your own. Think I'd better get help."

"How long since he left?"

"Oh, only about ten minutes. He can't have got far, but you don't know his route. He said he'd blow his whistle every now and again to see if you were near. The mists aren't bad, lassie! You must wait here. We'll find him for you."

Clem made to pick up the emergency telephone, but Angela, recovering from her first panic had had time to think.

133

Clem mentioning the whistle had given her an idea.

"Quick, Clem, your whistle."

Running back partway up the track Angela began to blow. Two short blasts, one short, one long, two shorts, three longs, three shorts and a long . . .

Back at the hut Clem listened, puzzled, but still Angela blew the whistle, then she stopped. All was silent.

"Please, Simon, answer," she breathed.

As she remembered the way they had parted that morning she felt her heart would break. Simon encouraged her love of the mountains, but only shared it to a lesser degree. He had only to slip on the scree, only take one wrong step . . .

Then, out of the mist-heavy silence came the sound she was praying for. One short blast, one long one, and another short. Simon had heard her. He would know she was safe!

By now Clem had joined her, and he looked at her, puzzled.

"And what was all that whistling about?"

"That's my little secret." Angela laughed. "Come on. Simon will be here soon and I'm frozen! Let's get that kettle on!"

ANGELA, warm in a borrowed woolly, stood at the hut door, her fingers cupped round a hot beaker of Bovril. When she saw the shadowy figure of her husband she ran to meet him.

"Oh, Simon! Never frighten me like that again," she told him, as he held her close.

"Oh, Angy! When I saw your haversack and remembered how you always made a point of taking it, I had to find you. I came home early to say I was sorry about this morning. I shouldn't have told you like that, but it doesn't matter now, love. As you say something will turn up here. I can't ask you to leave Calaby."

Angela smiled. Later they would talk. She would tell Simon about her quiet time on the mountain and the old stone church below. She would tell him that home was where *they* were together. Calaby would not go away, it would always be there waiting, and some day they would come, back, bring their children.

Together they walked towards the mountain hut.

"It was clever of you to think of our little secret code." Simon smiled and Angela grinned back.

They had been coming back from their honeymoon on the Isle of Skye, when, leaning over the rail of the ferry, Simon had first tapped out their little secret message. Angela had soon learned the Morse Code for *I love you.*

Now, often when they were not alone, Simon would tap the message out and she would smile and signal back, message received and understood. Then their eyes would meet and laughter would be very near the surface.

Today the message had had a special significance, and both their hearts were full as Simon took the mug his wife held out to him.

"Drink that, love," Angela said softly. "Then we'll go home." □

The Neglected Garden

TENDED by none save Father Time,
The rambling roses freely climb,
While pansies, thyme, in tangled mass
With mignonette, let no-one pass.

They're sheltered by old unpruned trees,
Bowing before the passing breeze,
Apple and pear, that in the spring
Their blossoms on the hard ground fling.

All through each sunny summer hour
Flit the bees from flower to flower,
Their dusty bodies to and fro
Scattering pollen as they go.

When evening comes and shadows fall,
Night draws her curtain on them all —
The fragrant flowers, the swaying trees
And drowsy humming of the bees.

— Marjorie Bell.

by
ELIZA YEAMAN

With Special Thanks To Grandpa

"COME on, Rhona, be a pal." Arthur Kane looked at his grand-daughter pleadingly. "I'm an old man and I don't look for much pleasure in life . . ."

"Now, Grandpa, don't be difficult." Rhona rubbed the iron briskly over a pillowcase. "You know fine I want to have everything perfect for Mum coming home on Saturday, and there's only tomorrow night left to get the polishing done. I simply must get through this ironing tonight!"

She folded the pillowcase but as she turned to put it on the table, she caught sight of her grandfather's downcast face. Then she looked at the clock — if she was going to give in it would have to be now, otherwise it would be too late for his game of dominoes at the club.

She picked one of her brother's shirts out of the ironing basket — and then looked again at her grandfather. He was silent now, believing that all his coaxing had been in vain. She sighed. She loved him dearly — she didn't want him to be sad. And after all, the last thing her mother had said before she went away was . . . "Be kind to Grandpa, now."

Grandpa could get around the house and the garden very well with his walking sticks but the distance to the club was too much for him to tackle. Usually Rhona's father took him along on a Thursday evening but Rhona herself had taken him last week — the first week of her parents' holiday. But she hadn't reckoned on taking him tonight . . .

However, she set the shirt down resignedly and stooped to unplug the iron.

"I expect I could finish this lot later," she said, and it was worth it to see the old man's face lighting up.

"I oiled my wheels this afternoon," he told her eagerly, "so you'll find the chair no bother to push."

Once they were outside in the evening sunshine Rhona, as if to make up for her earlier refusals, spoke to her grandfather cheerfully.

"I'm glad you prised me away from that ironing — it's lovely to be out."

"That's right, lass." The old man half turned in his wheelchair to smile up at her. "It's not good for a bonnie wee girl to be staying in every night and doing housework — it's enough to make you old before your time."

"It's only until Saturday." Rhona laughed. "You know that Mum hardly lets me do anything in the house. That's why I wanted everything to be perfect — to prove that I'm capable."

"Ay, your mother will go on holiday with an easier mind next year," Grandpa assured her. Then with a chuckle, he added, "Of course, you might be married by next year at this time."

Rhona's face turned bright pink and she replied with mock indignation.

"A year from now I'll still be struggling to choose between all those boyfriends you say I've got chasing me!"

Her grandfather enjoyed teasing her and Rhona could always give as good as she got. But tonight she had the feeling that there was something false, or forced about her laughter. Because while she was exchanging banter with her grandpa, she was also thinking about Don Crawford.

Twice now, Don Crawford had asked her to go out with him — and both times she'd had to refuse. On the first occasion, she had told him regretfully that she was busy all that week helping out every evening with the costumes for the church drama group.

"I'm an assistant wardrobe mistress," she had told him, and offered with a smile, "I could sell you a ticket for the play — if you like."

"No . . . no thanks." Don had blushed awkwardly as he replied. "At least, I don't mind buying a ticket if they are for a good cause. But I'm not all that keen on stage plays."

"Oh, well — in that case I won't sell you one," she had said, adding, "I would have had some trouble getting one anyhow, the shows are really popular."

He had blushed even more then, stammering apologies.

Rhona had tried to put him at ease. But he had never asked her out again — until today . . .

She had been on her way to the design department with an urgent file when he rose from his desk and spoke to her diffidently. She recalled vividly the look on his face which had caused her heart to skip a beat. But she hadn't had time to stop and chat with him . . . later, she might have been able to make him understand why she was too busy to go out with him tonight . . .

SHE stifled a sigh as she waited to wheel her grandfather's chair across the road. Don would never ask her for another date. She didn't know much about him. Some of the girls in the office said that he was brilliant at his work. But he was reserved and rather quiet.

Nobody knew quite what to make of him as he had only been in the office for a few months. But Rhona found it easy to guess that he was not the type to risk a third turn-down. It was not so easy to guess, though, why there was such a strange ache of disappointment in her heart when she thought about her hasty refusal this afternoon.

Inside the club she wheeled her grandfather towards his friends. He was a popular figure and she soon left him with his cronies and went off in search of some young company.

A table tennis match was in progress. She saw that her brother, John, was playing — and looking like winning. She watched with a group of friends then someone mentioned that there was to be dancing after the table tennis. But Rhona said she would be gone by then.

"Please stay, Rhona," Greg Buist coaxed her. "I've brought along some new tapes — fabulous music!"

Rhona was surprised at Greg singling her out but she shook her head.

"I'm only here on escort duty," she explained. "When Grandpa goes home — I go, too."

"Are your parents still away?" Greg gave her a sympathetic smile. "Are you still head cook and bottle washer?"

"Plus all the rest of the chores." She nodded, and then with a glance in her brother's direction, added, "John's always willing to help — the only trouble is he seldom notices what needs to be done. He has to be told."

"A typical male?" Greg queried with a twinkle.

"You could say that," Rhona agreed with a broad smile, and turned her attention back to the game.

Her brother won and she was among those congratulating him, when Greg Buist, his arm casually around Rhona's shoulder, spoke again.

"How about doing us a favour, John? Would you take your

▶ *over*

according to Custom

IN ancient times Hallowe'en was regarded as the last night of the year by the Gaelic people. It was then that they held their main festival, and being sun-worshippers lit great bonfires to revive the dying sun. People also remembered their departed relatives, and it's this association with the supernatural that is carried on today in various parts of the country. In Scotland children dress up in costumes and go "guising," where they go round the neighbourhood in fancy dress and do a little party piece for a small novelty reward.

grandfather home — and let Rhona stay for the dancing?"

John gave a small shrug.

"OK, I don't mind." Then giving them one of his cheeky grins he enquired, "If I take Grandpa home, who will take Rhona home?"

Greg's hand tightened on her shoulder as she began to protest that she didn't want to stay, she had too much to do. But he was assuring her brother.

"*I'll* take Rhona home. Don't let that worry you!"

"But maybe I should worry," John quipped. "She's my little sister — and I'm supposed to look out for her."

"Of all the nerve!" Rhona exclaimed. But she couldn't sustain her anger in the midst of the merriment around her.

And despite her reluctance, she did enjoy staying on for the impromptu dance, the music from Greg's new tapes was as good as he had promised.

★   ★   ★   ★

It was almost midnight when they walked home together. Greg lived in the next street. He had often walked her home. But tonight, there was something different in the atmosphere between them. Rhona sensed that Greg would put his arms around her at the garden gate.

She lifted her face to his and their good night kiss was sweet and warm and tender.

"I love you, Rhona," Greg murmured softly.

She moved gently out of his embrace.

"I like you too, Greg — you are one of my best friends," she said, and could tell that he was hurt by her words. But it was kinder she thought to give him no false hopes.

Perhaps he imagined he was in love with her, she mused, as she said good night and went indoors.

There was a light showing under her grandfather's bedroom door. He was sitting up in bed reading, waiting for her return.

"Are you all right, Grandpa?" she asked quietly. "Would you like some cocoa?"

"No thanks, I'm fine," he told her. "We had some sandwiches — John kept one for you. It's wrapped up in the fridge.

"I'll leave it for the morning," Rhona answered. "Good night, Grandpa. Don't be reading too long now."

In her own room, she set the alarm for six o'clock so that she'd have plenty of time to finish the ironing before she went to work.

But as she lay restlessly awake, she was wishing that she had tackled the ironing tonight instead of leaving it until the morning. She was far too keyed up to sleep. All sorts of thoughts and ideas were rushing about inside her head. But nothing sensible, nothing that her brain could catch hold of . . .

That oddly-questioning look in Grandpa's eyes, for instance. And why hadn't he teased her about Greg Buist? And Greg had told her that he loved her.

Perhaps she loved him too in a way. He was great fun, a super dancer, always ready with a laugh. But love is different, she told herself.

Falling in love means fire, passion and enchantment. And anguish, she thought, as an image of Don Crawford came into her mind, bringing that helpless sensation of longing which had become so familiar to her. Why, why, why was she so fated to lose him before she really had the chance to get to know him?

There was an attraction which drew them — and a chemistry which caused them to blush and stumble over their words when they were near to each other — as if powerful emotions were waiting to be unleashed. But there was no chance of that happening now . . .

Sleep claimed her at last but her dreams were sad and filled with tears of yearning.

A T the office next morning, her mood of despondency was still with her. If she leaned away from her typewriter and craned her neck, she could see Don Crawford at the desk nearest to the swing doors. If only he would look up . . . but he didn't.

She wondered if she would spend the rest of her life longing for the moment when their eyes might meet.

> ## Life's Loveliness
>
> F ULL many a lovely flower has bloomed
>   Far from the haunts of men,
> And spent its perfume on the air,
>   In some secluded glen.
>
> And many a blossom rich and sweet,
>   That lured the honey bee,
> Has cast its beauty, all unseen,
>   From off some woodland tree.
>
> How oft a kindly thought unsaid,
>   Or good deed left undone —
> Lost in the fray of a busy day —
>   Might have cheered someone.
>
> Waste not the loveliness of life
>   But share it while you may:
> Let not the things of less import
>   Steal happiness away!
>
>   — Patricia McGavock.

She gave herself a mental shake. Stop acting like a fool, Rhona Kane, she commanded herself. If you fancy the man, have the courage to talk to him. And if he is so very shy, what's to hinder *you* asking *him* for a date?

It was simpler than she expected. She knew that he never ate in the staff canteen. So all she did was put her coat on and stop by his desk to tell him with a friendly smile that she was planning to eat out for once.

"I generally go to a fast-food place just off the High Street," Don told her, and offered, "I'll take you there, if you like."

Rhona was delighted and it was obvious that Don was also pleased, although they didn't find much to say to each other as they hurried along. Speed was necessary since they only had an hour for lunch . . .

Afterwards, Rhona decided that it must surely have been the longest hour of her life — and the most disappointing.

"What a bore for you," Don had said after she'd explained in detail the reasons for not being free to go out with him the previous evening.

Chilled, Rhona had assured him that it was a pleasure for her to be able to take over the reins of the household so that her parents could have a much-needed holiday.

"Yes, well, I suppose it is nice to do a good deed." Don had nodded pensively, evidently impressed by her vehemence. But then he'd added with a wry grin, "Still, it must be a bit of a drag — what with the ancient grandfather in the wheelchair and all."

Rhona drew in a deep breath . . . then she decided that it would be wiser to change the subject.

"So where did you go last night?" she asked him rather tremulously.

"The cinema," Don answered promptly. "I always go to the pictures on a Thursday — you missed a really worthwhile film last night."

He was still expounding on the merits of the film's artistic direction when they arrived back at the office just before two o'clock.

They hastily said goodbye before going their separate ways.

The Common Path

A TANGLED and uneven path it was,
  Tall hedged by hawthorn, birch
  and ancient beech;
A secret and enchanted place — and
    more —
  A solitary way far out of reach.
It sheltered life in limb and branch and
    leaf —
  A dappled world of sunlight and soft
shade;
Yet people full of purpose passed it by
  And never saw beyond the gentle
    glade.
But should they cast an eye or bend and
    ear —
  Pay homage to the work of nature's
    wrath,
And listen to the whispers of the land —
  They'd find the world within the
    common path.
          — *Sylvia Mountain.*

★   ★   ★   ★

Rhona was rather glad to escape to the typing which was her afternoon's work. But inevitably her thoughts began winging away from the dull notes which she was transcribing.

She was thinking of the warmth and the laughter which seemed to surround Greg Buist. And she was thinking of his gentleness and kindness — the caring qualities which he possessed.

Last night Greg would never have persuaded her to stay late at the club if he hadn't made certain first that her grandfather would be well looked after.

All through the afternoon, impressions of Greg were slipping in and out of her mind. It was as if telling her he loved her had somehow altered her views of him, highlighted her affinity with him.

At five o'clock, Don Crawford was lingering by his desk, which was unusual — he was normally one of the first to leave the office. So often she had glanced sadly at his empty place longing for another glimpse of him. But now, as she walked past with a group of colleagues, she was merely one of a cheerful bunch saying good night to him.

There was no blush on her cheeks, no fluttering of her heart. In reply to Sandra Mollison, who remarked that he was still the dishiest man in the office, Rhona said airily.

"He's not my type."

The words released a fine sensation of freedom in her. All her fantasies about him were fogotten, the mysterious magic had quite suddenly vanished.

Later that evening, she was on her knees polishing the hall surround when the phone rang. She thought it would be her parents but it was Greg.

She wasn't sure if it was jumping up so quickly that made her suddenly light headed and giddy or if it was the sound of his voice which had this oddly-pleasant effect on her. She sat down on the floor to chat to him . . .

Grandpa opened the sitting-room door and then discreetly closed it again. But now she was not surprised that he didn't get up to his usual trick of teasing her.

Grandpa is a wise old man, she thought lovingly, he must know there is something serious in the air. □

Cupid was a Teddy Bear!

A S the hands of the wall clock crept towards seven-thirty Vicki hoped she didn't look as tired as she felt. There were still some late shoppers browsing about the toy department. Tomorrow was Christmas Eve and after tonight she would have two whole days off duty.

Her feet felt like lead weights, and all she could think of was the sanctuary of the flat and the bliss of a hot bath. But being a number one sales girl in Waterson's store meant looking cool, efficient and cheerful, no matter what.

There had been gremlins about all day — a faulty cash register, an old lady who fainted on the escalator, and a small boy who had knocked down a stand full of glass baubles.

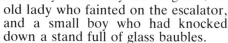

by S. W. RAEBURN

But long as the day might be, the glittering scene still held a kind of magic for her. And over there, in the realm of the dolls, woolly animals and teddy bears, the real essence of Christmas seemed to be embodied. It was old fashioned, she knew, but it said so much more to her than the ranks of boxed games and computer toys.

STANDING out, foremost amongst them all, was Humphrey, the giant teddy bear. He had been on show for nearly two months and no-one had bought him. The truth was, he was very expensive and very, very beautiful and cuddly — golden yellow, with limpid brown eyes and an expression that made you think he was about to burst out laughing. Or so it seemed to Vicki.

He wasn't spreadeagled or rigid, but actually sitting there with a red bow tie under his chin and wearing a pair of green, short trousers. Someone with inspiration had given him a pair of horn-rimmed spectacles so that he looked human and wise.

Somewhere inside Vicki Burns was a little girl who would have liked to own him. He was a friend whom she greeted in the mornings, and whom she bade "Good night" when she switched off the lights at closing time.

145

The People's Friend Annual

By seven o'clock the prospective customers had thinned out to a handful, and Vicki could take a minute or two to sit down thankfully by her desk. That was when she noticed the tall man. He was casually dressed, though the loose windcheater jacket had the cut of good tailoring, but it was the way he moved that held her interest.

He didn't loiter like someone looking for ideas. He strode swiftly past the shelves of mechanical toys and space-age novelties, only pausing once or twice to look around as if in search of something.

The tan on his face had not been got from the long-past European summer. He must have been abroad, Vicki thought. Suddenly his eyes, steady and discerning, caught hers and she hurriedly looked away.

It seemed only seconds later when as if by magic he was standing there, in front of her. What made her gasp with something like shock was the fact that under his arm was Humphrey, the life-size bear. Held horizontally with his spectacles askew, to Vicki Humphrey presented a picture of outraged dignity.

THE man's face, which had seemed forbidding in repose, now struck her as attractive. He was one of those people who could smile with his eyes. He hitched Humphrey to an upright position and sat him on the desk.

"Can you help me?" he enquired. "I'd like to buy this chap."

Vicki collected herself swiftly, brushing aside a slight sadness at the prospect of the bear's departure.

"Certainly, sir," she replied helpfully. "I think Humphrey will be glad to find a home at last."

"Humphrey?" The customer's smile broadened. "Why do you call him that?"

"It's his name. All bears have to have a name. With this one it's built in." Vicki reached over and poked a finger against the furry stomach.

"My name is Humphrey!" the bear declared in a rich baritone.

"There's a trap-door which conceals a battery in the small of his back," Vicki explained. "He says that every time you squeeze him."

"It's for a little girl of three." The man produced his wallet and selected a credit card. "Do you think that's all right? Won't she think he's too huge?"

"Oh, no," Vicki replied with conviction. "To a child of that age, a big teddy bear is something almost real. He could take the place of some imaginary character children often create in their minds. I'm sure your little girl will love him."

"Well, she's not *my* little girl," he corrected her. "I'm her godfather." Then his eyes lit with a new interest. "You seem to know a lot about children."

"I don't really. It's just that when I was a little girl . . . ." Vicki felt the colour rise in her cheeks. She paused, embarrassed. He wouldn't want to know about her early years in an orphanage, about the void in her life which had bred a longing for something or somebody that was strictly her own. Instead she busied herself with the payment, and a swift look at the signed counterfoil told her his name was L. J. Grant.

Cupid Was A Teddy Bear!

Wrapping Humphrey threatened to be quite an operation. He was an almost impossible parcel, and in the end L. J. Grant intervened.

"Never mind the wrappings," he said. "I'll take him away in a taxi. Tomorrow's Christmas Eve, and he must be delivered tonight."

His eyes held hers again and she thought he was about to say more. Then the moment passed, and with a nod and a smile he was gone.

SUSAN sighed and wondered about L. J. Grant. Somehow she felt as if her day had just been turned upside down. It was a long time since she had met a man who radiated this sense of warmth.

Since the day two years ago, when Denis had died just a week before their wedding, she had held herself aloof from the men she met. So why should she have this sudden, empty feeling as she watched L. J. Grant leave?

Humphrey, of course, had gone too. The empty space, where he had sat regarding her through his plain glass spectacles, added to Vicki's sense of loss. But that, she told herself, was simply childish. After all, she was twenty-five years old!

Still, the interlude had brought the end of the working day nearer. In half an hour she would be on her way back to the flat she shared with Morna Aston, who was a ward sister in a paediatric hospital.

Tonight the two of them would spend an hour or two in the flat putting up decorations, dressing the Christmas tree and cooking a late supper. Then by tomorrow evening Morna would be gone to her boyfriend's home for a family gathering, leaving Vicki with only sketchy plans for the Christmas break.

Apart from an ageing aunt in Canada, Vicki had no family ties, and without Denis to share it with her, Christmas had become something of an ordeal, haunted by poignant memories.

There were, of course, open invitations to several parties from thoughtful friends who always included her at times like this. She was grateful for that, but it wasn't like having a sense of belonging.

AT last it was closing time, and Vicki went mechanically through the routine check-ups and safety precautions. Drenching rain greeted her as she let herself out through the main doors. There

Easter

EARTH is a bride at Eastertide,
With blossoms in her hair,
Over the land the pealing bells
Ring out her wedding air.

Bright is her smile and soft her tread
On this most lovely day,
Breezes blow gently as she goes
Upon her perfumed way.

Sunlight is in our hearts again,
And joyous hymns are sung.
Earth is a bride at Eastertide
When all the world is young.

Eileen Thomas.

147

was nothing for it but to wait in the shelter of the awning until she could hail a taxi. On a night like this it wouldn't be easy.

She had only been waiting a few minutes when a man sprinted across the road and joined her on the steps of the store. He was carrying something bulky wrapped in what looked like a raincoat, and it was only when he stood panting in front of her that she recognised L. J. Grant.

He was hatless and she could see raindrops trickling down his nose.

"I suppose I'm too late," he said breathlessly. "I was hoping to find the place still open."

"Is there anything wrong?" Vicki tried to gather her wits, still uncomprehending. "You're the gentleman who bought Humphrey — the teddy bear, I mean — aren't you?"

He lifted one end of the macintosh to reveal the placid, furry face of Humphrey.

"Well, just about everything has gone wrong," he began. "I arrived here in London today from Brazil, all set for an old-fashioned Christmas. The idea was to make a surprise visit to old friends who made me their daughter's godfather.

"When I rang them from my hotel after I left you, a complete stranger answered the telephone. He said he was now tenant of their house. My friend, Bill, has moved abroad with his family. His firm suddenly posted him to Canada three weeks ago, and they'll be there for at least two years."

He smiled ruefully. "The question is, what do I do with this bear? I can't expect you to take it back, I suppose?"

IN spite of the rain and her fatigue, Vicki was half-amused by his helplessness. But she was also rather touched.

"Well," she said, after a few moments' thought. "You could bring him back and exchange him for goods to the same value or more in the toy department. Or I might be able to arrange that you open an account with us and have credit marked up to you to the value of Humphrey."

L. J. Grant stood there undecided, the expression on his face a little woebegone.

"I suppose so," he said, but with an obvious lack of enthusiasm. "I expect that's what I ought to do." Then he moved closer to Vicki. "Look, I don't really care about the money," he said earnestly. "It's just . . . well, I had this good feeling about Christmas and now I've lost it. This teddy bear . . . Humphrey . . . you'll think I'm mad, but now that my plans have collapsed I feel I want to give it away to some child who would be really happy to have it." He laughed to cover his embarrassment.

"Of course, it would be quite crazy to walk up to some little kid in the street and say, 'Hello, this is for you.' Their parents would probably call the police, or I'd get a punch on the nose!"

Vicki suppressed a giggle.

"I see your point," she agreed. "But there are still children around who aren't lucky enough to have much at Christmas time. There are ways of seeing that a toy goes to a particular child who otherwise

Cupid Was A Teddy Bear!

wouldn't have it." She moved away from him. "Anyway, we really can't talk about it now. It's late, and . . ."

"I'm sorry," he broke in. "I really am being a bore, and you must be very tired. How long have you been in that store today?"

"Twelve hours, give or take a little." Vicki felt herself wilting again. "And I have some cooking to do when I go home."

"I could kick myself for bothering you, but you're the only person I felt I could turn to." He was contrite. "Could you possibly agree to have dinner with me, right now? You must be starving, and we could talk about what I'm going to do with Humphrey. That is, if you're not otherwise engaged."

Vicki took about five seconds to make up her mind. The evening arrangement with Morna wasn't binding. She had to admit L. J. Grant's behaviour had been impeccable — and she *was* hungry.

"All right," she said. "Thank you. I'd like that." And as if to make sure she couldn't change her mind, an empty taxi approached from the nearby traffic lights.

"We'll have to take Humphrey along with us," L. J. Grant said. "We haven't time to take him back to my hotel."

IN no time at all Vicki was sitting in a cab close to L. J. Grant, who was now wearing his raincoat. Humphrey the bear, in his bow tie and green shorts, was leaning drunkenly against the door. His spectacles had slipped down a little and his brown eyes seemed to regard her with a look of profound wisdom.

"I haven't been in London for four years," her escort was saying, "so my knowledge of restaurants is out of date, but I used to know a good one in Charlotte Street."

By the time they arrived she knew his name was Lester and that his years in Brazil had been spent helping to build a dam. The restaurant was French and Vicki liked it on sight. She also liked the way Lester carried in the bear as if it were the most natural thing in the world for him to do.

The head waiter smiled a welcome, unperturbed by the presence of Humphrey.

"It'll have to be a table for three," Lester declared. "I'd rather not leave the teddy bear in the cloakroom. He represents a problem we have to solve." He smiled. "Anyway, he's used to being on show!"

The restaurant was three-quarters full, and when Humphrey was safely seated, heads began to turn in their direction, until Vicki found herself wishing there had been time to change and do her face and hair properly. After her long day in Waterson's store she was sure she must look like someone who had slept in a haystack.

"I must look a fright," she said, hiding behind the enormous menu.

"You look perfectly beautiful," Lester assured her. "And so does Humphrey. It's a case of beauty and the beast."

"Maybe so, but I wonder which of us looks more like the beast!" Vicki grimaced.

As the wine and the excellent food began to build up Vicki's strength

149

and morale, she felt the strain of the long day vanish. And the longer she sat opposite the strong reassuring figure of L. J. Grant, the more she liked what she saw.

THERE was something confident and calm about him that lifted her heart and made her feel less lonely. He was only a passing stranger, she reminded herself firmly. But since his Christmas plans had been ruined and she herself had none, Humphrey had done them both a good turn.

"About Humphrey," she said at last. "It's a little late to find a home for him tonight. But I can give you the name of a children's hospital where my flat-mate works," she offered. "I've met the matron, who's a very nice woman. I'm sure they'd be glad to accept him. He would be ideal for the permanent toy nursery which is in use all the time."

Lester considered this.

"So he wouldn't actually belong to someone," he said finally.

"Probably not," Vicki agreed. "But I do know a group of local women who get together every year and collect toys, or make them, to give to individual children who aren't as well off as others. I can give you the organiser's address." From her handbag she took a used envelope and a pen and scribbled on the back.

"That sounds promising," Lester said as he glanced at the envelope. "You seem to understand what I have in mind."

By the time they were sipping their coffee at the end of the meal Vicki, in a relaxed mood, found herself telling Lester about her childhood.

"Before I was adopted I lived in an orphanage and, though I always wanted a *big* teddy bear, I never, ever got one, so I suppose that's why I'm a bit sentimental about them."

A soberness crossed Lester Grant's face, like the shadow of some far distant memory.

"I really don't know much about children, I suppose," he murmured. "I only had one for two years."

"You're married, then?" Vicki's eyes widened. Somehow she hadn't thought so.

"Was," he replied tersely. "Before I began looking for jobs in odd corners of the world. We were on holiday in Cornwall and one morning I went off on my own to see an old friend in Truro. My wife and small daughter went on a coach tour round the coast." He paused. "I never saw them again. The coach went out of control and they were both killed."

Tears stung her eyes as Vicki began to understand exactly why Lester wanted to make a child happy — some real, tangible child, although it was not his own.

"I'm sorry," she said at last. "I had a feeling — I knew there must be something . . ."

"I'll order more coffee," he said. "This stuff has gone cold." And as so often happens at times like these, the next minute brought them both back to coping with absurdities.

Cupid Was A Teddy Bear!

THE waitress, galvanised by Lester's signal, came hurrying over. Her shoes, perhaps unsuited for swift movement, caught in the carpet and she stumbled into Humphrey's chair, knocking the bear to the floor and against the table leg.

Eyes and heads turned once more to their table. From somewhere on the floor, activated by the impact, came the rich baritone of the bear's total vocabulary, "My name is Humphrey!"

There was a ripple of laughter from adjoining tables so, with Humphrey rescued and the waitress reassured, it wasn't long before Vicki and Lester were out on the street again.

"That was fun," Vicki said. "I'll always remember this evening." It had stopped raining, but Lester looked a little forlorn, standing there with the bear almost upside down under his arm.

"Does it have to finish here?" he asked. "Look, it's really quite early. There's rather a good film showing at Leicester Square. If the timing's right we might just catch the last performance."

For Vicki the past two hours had banished weariness and brought a vitality she had not felt for a long time. The prospect of prolonging this one pleasant evening was too strong to resist.

"What about Humphrey?"

"Don't worry about that," he said confidently. "We'll fit him in somehow."

▶ *over*

according to Custom

UNTIL the 1800s Christmas trees were virtually unknown in this country and it was largely due to Prince Albert placing a tree in Windsor Castle that the practice caught on. Our picture shows the lovely tree in Trafalgar Square, which since 1947 has been a gift from the people of Oslo as a way of expressing thanks for the Norwegian exiles who found hospitality here during the Second World War.

And so it was that after another taxi ride they arrived, complete with bear, at the cinema box office. The cashier slid two tickets towards Lester.

Producing another three pounds, he lifted Humphrey from the floor and presented his furry face at the window.

"We'll need another one," he told her. "There are three of us."

"You can't have a seat for a thing like that." The girl's eyes flew open with shock. "At least, I don't think so. If the place fills up and we need the seat, it can't be occupied by a teddy bear!"

"But we're paying for it." Lester was adamant. "And if that's the rule, we can squeeze him down to the floor in an emergency."

The girl shook her head, but reluctantly produced another ticket.

Down Memory Lane

WHAT a store of memories the years have treasured up.
Happy times and sorrows have been neatly folded up.
Until one day we reminisce, and, strange as it may seem,
It's nearly always happy things that pop up from our dreams.

Little things from childhood often creep in to the fore,
Birthday treats and Christmas trees with presents by the score.
Then the major happenings will often strike a chord —
The day we gained promotion, or the time we went abroad.

Memory lanes are winding ones we love to wander through.
Faces long forgotten will come smiling back at you.
Loneliness is overcome, we meet old friends again.
Breathe a prayer of thankfulness for having memory lane.
— E. Horscroft.

THE film was obviously going to be good. It was a deeply emotional romance which had collected three Oscars, and the first half-hour took it to a point where the girl had decided to send away her lover rather than let him find out that she was going blind.

It was during this scene that Humphrey began to topple slowly forward, threatening to bring his head in contact with the shoulder of the man in the seat in front.

Lester shot out a hand and caught him just in time, but unfortunately by the stomach. The small recording disc inside the bear went relentlessly into action.

The nearby section of the audience was startled, to say the least, by the penetrating voice of the bear announcing that his name was Humphrey.

Just one of these growling interruptions might have been only a mild distraction, but to the horror of both Humphrey's guardians, the sound

152

Cupid Was A Teddy Bear!

track kept repeating: "My name is Humphrey! My name is Humphrey! My name is Humphrey!"

Amidst indignant protests from adjacent seats, Lester grabbed Vicki's arm with one hand and Humphrey's with the other.

"Let's get out of here fast!" he whispered urgently.

As they squeezed their way to the aisle and then to the exit Lester muffled Humphrey's voice in the folds of his raincoat. Out on the street they paused for breath, then dissolved into helpless laughter.

Vicki opened the flap in Humphrey's back and removed the battery.

"I think he's done enough talking for one night. But it shouldn't be difficult to have him repaired."

Lester aimed a mock left hook at Humphrey's innocent and placid face.

"He has certainly given you a hard day," he apologised. "And I'm afraid I've been rather a nuisance myself."

"I wouldn't have missed it for anything." Vicki handed him the now-silent bear. "But I'll miss Humphrey now he's not in the store."

THE next free taxi took them to the entrance of Vicki's flat. When Lester got out and stood with her on the pavement she was aware this casual but memorable evening had now reached its inevitable conclusion.

Tomorrow was Christmas Eve, and as far as she knew, Lester was adrift, like herself in this vast city, alone and unattached. Yet a natural reticence told her that it was not for her to hint that they might meet again.

Quickly, she found a scrap of paper and wrote the address of the hospital and Morna's ward.

"Good luck then, with finding a home for Humphrey," she said. "I suppose you'll be moving on somewhere?"

"Nowhere to move to," he replied. "No family now, and all I have in this town is a bank account, a lawyer and a desk in my firm's head office. But right now, all I need is sleep."

Vicki saw with concern that his face was pallid and his eyes heavy with fatigue. It suddenly hit her with force that only this morning he had flown in from South America. He looked almost pathetic standing there with the giant toy bear in his arms. A wave of sadness brought a tightness to her throat.

"Goodbye, then. Perhaps you'll let me know what happens to Humphrey." She watched the taxi all the way down the street until it vanished round a corner.

Inside the flat the trappings of Christmas seemed tawdry and pointless. Morna had started dressing their small tree and hanging up decorations, but had gone to bed early.

In the heavy silence, Vicki wished there had been someone to talk to. Those hours with Lester Grant had meant more to her than she wanted to admit. He had stirred in her something she had given up as lost.

She was preparing a hot drink when the sound of the doorbell made her start with surprise. She hoped fervently it wasn't some well-meaning friend returning from a party in convivial mood. After today, it was the last thing she needed.

WHEN she opened the door she could hardly believe that L. J. Grant was really standing on the doorstep, still holding the bear. But by then she was getting used to the unexpected.

"Come in and have some coffee," she invited. "I'm just making it."

"I had to come back," he said. "I stopped the taxi because something suddenly dawned on me. After tonight I couldn't even look at Humphrey without thinking of you. Giving him away on Christmas Eve would be pointless unless we did it together."

He set the bear down on the nearest chair. With his bow tie askew, Humphrey looked like a reveller who had dined more well than wisely.

"I'm afraid we've lost his spectacles somewhere," Lester added lamely, "but he's still in one piece."

Vicki's heart had begun to thump wildly. The room, previously dull despite its festive trimmings, appeared to sparkle now, and come alive.

"I wasn't looking forward to tomorrow," she admitted. "But it feels like Christmas now. When you've had enough sleep at the hotel, come back here and we'll go in search of Humphrey's new owner. Then I'll cook a celebration dinner."

He came and stood beside her and it seemed natural that he took her hand.

"I was wondering how I could survive Christmas in a strange hotel," he murmured. "But Humphrey has solved everything!"

He punched the bear's midriff, but this time Humphrey said nothing. He only stared ahead with his soft brown eyes and seemed to smile secretly. □

Christmas Celebration

U PON the quiet hills above the town,
　　Keeping their watch,
The shepherds huddle the fire round,
Keeping their watch.
The bright stars shine on fleece of white.
Their lonely vigil keeping.
And brighter of hope throughout the
　　night,
The men of wisdom seeking.

Seeking a king to rule over all.
Salvation to sinners.
Bringing to those who hear the call,
Salvation to sinners.
There in the stable the lowly maid,
Birth to the Lord is giving.
And through his birth the pathway is
　　laid,
The Christian way of living.

Loud the hosannas sound from the skies.
Angels are watching
Over the Babe, where in a stable he lies.
Angels are watching.
Join in the song the angels sing,
Joy to mankind they pray.
Happiness, Peace and Love to bring
Jesus is born this day.

— *Phyllis Heath.*

A FACE FROM THE PAST

by DEBBIE RITCHIE

"BUT you *can't* marry a man you don't love," Linda Clark said firmly. "And you can't love him to order, just because . . . because . . ."

Halted by Veronica's expression, Linda looked across the table in the living-room of the flat they shared and sighed helplessly.

"But I do *like* him very much," Veronica said earnestly. "And I admire him so much, too. He's kind, and he's fun but . . ."

"But that isn't enough," Linda said bluntly. "And you know it in your heart. Oh, I know it all sounds so romantic, especially to other people, because he fished you out of that lake all those years ago. And if he hadn't you might have drowned."

Linda sighed. "I can understand how you'll always feel so thankful and grateful."

"I don't know how I can face him when . . . if . . ." Veronica's expression was haunted. "I just know from the way he spoke, the way he kissed me last night, when he brought me back from the youth club. I just know that soon, maybe next time, he's going to ask me. Maybe when we go to the ballet on Saturday.

"Oh! Linda, I feel so scared of hurting him, so ashamed of myself. If only we could just go on being pals, going around with the others, and you and Joe."

"If only," Linda put in succinctly, "he hadn't come back into your life

157

so suddenly. If he'd never come here to work. But what's the use of if only . . ."

Yes, Veronica thought. And yet they'd all had such a good time together. And at first it had been such fun — a lovely surprise to meet Rod again when she was doing her stint taking round the leaflets asking young people to help repair and decorate the old hall which was to be used for the youth club.

But they were asking not just for help, but for donations of paint, brushes, varnish, wood — even sand and cement. Veronica had drafted the leaflet, dividing one side into days of the week so volunteers could fill in which days they had free.

Then, with her boss's permission, she'd run them off on the photo-copier in her office.

At the bottom, she had included the request *Please send all offers to Veronica Watt*, with her phone number, and the address of the little flat she shared with Linda.

She'd also sent one to her parents' farm, circling the word *wood* in red, with the hint that if they had any left over from the barn they'd been repairing, maybe one of her brothers could bring it over in the van!

Most of the leaflets she'd just pushed through the letterboxes of houses, except those where she knew the people and stopped to have a word.

When she'd come to a small end-of-terrace house where a young man was weeding the front garden, she just handed over the leaflet.

"If you could help at all," she'd said politely, "we'd all be very grateful."

She was just walking away, noting thankfully that he was reading it, and thinking well, that was *one* that wouldn't be stuffed behind the mantelpiece clock and forgotten — when he called after her.

"Veronica Watt . . . wait a moment please. Do you know Veronica?"

"Sometimes!" She'd laughed. "Though other times I do wonder. Should I know you? Were you at Southdown School?"

Somehow, she thought, he does look vaguely familiar. But she couldn't place him.

Swiftly he'd put a hand on her shoulder.

"No, you wouldn't be likely to remember me," he'd said. Maybe you won't even remember Roderick Macrae . . . but they call me Rod!"

Veronica had looked at him awed, and excited. "As if I wouldn't remember the boy who saved my life . . ."

INSTANTLY, she'd had a vision of that moment, on her eighth birthday, falling over some loose stones and down into the lake, where her family had driven for a picnic.

Typically, the self-reliant farmer's daughter, she'd wandered off to gather wild flowers for a garland.

She'd never forgotten her terror, so sure she was drowning, until she felt someone grip her and drag her to safety.

Her twelve-year-old rescuer, embarrassed by all the fuss, had swiftly disappeared back to his family, who he said were a mile or so down the road. But not before Veronica's dad had found out his name and thanked him.

"But he wouldn't accept a gift," her dad had said at the time. "He was quite gruff. Wouldn't talk about it, and said please don't follow him and tell his family. 'It was nothing . . . anyone would have done the same . . .' "

"Nice boy," her mother added, "bless him." Then of course she'd been "roasted" for going too far away and taking chances!

Often Veronica had thought about that day, and her carelessness. Often she'd remembered and felt those tough little hands pulling her to safety, though she could hardly remember his face or anything about him.

And now, here he was, standing in front of her.

"I've always been so grateful," she said. "You were so quick . . . so wonderful."

"Oh! Shucks." He laughed. "I was scared stiff your dad might follow me and find out . . . well I lied, you see. I'd sneaked out with one of my uncles to go fishing!" He began to laugh at the memory. "I've reformed, though, honest!"

"Isn't life strange," Veronica murmured, "to meet you again like this when I'm scrounging about for help?"

He'd leaned on his spade and told her about his job in the accounts department of the supermarket — one of a chain belonging to a huge company.

Night

A S I drew back the curtains what a wonderful sight
Lay before my eyes in the still of the night.
The ground was a carpet of untrodden snow,
The street lamps shone brightly and set it aglow.
I stood by the window and felt such a thrill
To witness the world so quiet and still —
No movement or noise, just the earth gleaming white.
A magical peace was around me that night.

— Norah Dickin.

"They moved me here about a year ago, and I was so lucky to find digs in this house — a nice young couple with a couple of kids. The husband is a policeman, with awkward shift times, so they're quite glad of some help in the garden — and it's a nice change after working with figures all day!"

She'd told him about her job as secretary in a building firm. And before she'd moved on to deliver the rest of the leaflets he'd promised to come and help.

"I'm quite a dab hand with a paintbrush, and a saw, so you've got yourself a volunteer! It's lovely to see you again after all these years. Makes me think," he added with a rueful smile, "I was a bit of a mug to run away so fast!"

159

A ND since then, Veronica thought in bed that night, after her talk with Linda, he'd been so helpful, and so constructive — as well as being fun to be with.

If only he hadn't got so serious last night. She'd been so totally surprised . . . so shocked . . . and so terribly sorry, for she'd never thought of him in that way. And then he'd just gone striding off down the road as if he was as terrified as she'd been when she'd thought she would drown.

Maybe, Veronica thought, that analogy wasn't so surprising either. For undoubtedly, Rod had been tremendously shaken by emotion.

Since one youthful romance foundered, Veronica hadn't really been interested in anyone, but she enjoyed her job, and the friendship of boys at the club.

But that was all.

And now . . . ? At last she dropped off to sleep, still wondering what on earth she would say to Rod if he did speak of his feelings when they went to the ballet on Saturday.

It was "Swan Lake," and they both loved the music. When Rod took her hand, and held it through most of the performance, she hadn't the heart to pull it away.

He walked her home in the moonlight across the park. Her heart stopped when he stood still by the lake and turned to her.

"Veronica," he said, "I have something to tell you."

For the life of her she couldn't find words to respond. But it was as if he hadn't noticed her silence, for he went on.

"I . . . I'm afraid I won't be able to help out any more at the club . . ."

This was so unexpected, she almost shouted, "But why? What's happened?"

"The firm is sending me to another . . . another branch," he said.

At last Veronica got her breath back, and she didn't know whether to laugh or cry — with shock.

"A long way from here, I take it?" she asked him.

"Yes, on the South Coast. Actually . . . it looks as if they'll be moving me around a bit."

"Promotion?" she asked.

He hesitated. "Well, in the end yes, I believe so."

"Oh, Rod," she said, "I'm so glad for you." She was just going to add that she . . . all of them, would miss him. But stopped herself in time.

"You deserve it," she added.

"Bless you," he said lightly. "So this visit of ours to 'Swan Lake' was a sort of swan song. But it's been fun meeting again, hasn't it?"

"Oh, yes," she said, and she felt her voice was shaking oddly. Well, it was the surprise, she thought.

"It has, and everyone is enormously grateful for all your help. When are you going?"

"Monday . . . well, I'm leaving here tomorrow night," he said.

"So soon . . . ?" Veronica became immensely practical. "Then we'd better get back home pronto. You'll be wanting to do your packing — must be an awful rush to get everything ready in time."

At the door of the flat, she just swiftly put out her hand, shook his and wished him "all the luck in the world."

"I'm no good at writing," he said, "so I won't, Veronica."

"That's OK," she said, though conscious of a faint disappointment. "Two happy ships passing in the night . . ."

LINDA was waiting up for her.

"Well," she asked, "did you find the courage to turn down his proposal, after all?"

Veronica suddenly began to laugh, quite hysterically.

"I must have got it all wrong," she said breathlessly, at last. "He was so intense, the other night. And at the ballet tonight, he did hold my hand all through. But then, he was almost casual . . ."

She told Linda about his going away.

"Oh well," Linda said when she'd finished, "I daresay he was excited the other night. Perhaps he'd just heard the news about his move and the promotion to come, and then, realising he'd gone a bit over the top . . ."

Linda paused, and added, "Unless . . ."

"Unless what?"

"Well, your face is pretty expressive. Maybe he saw the shock in it, maybe he realised you didn't care. Maybe that's why he's going away, 'cos he could see you didn't care for him except as a friend."

Veronica didn't answer for a few moments. Then she said thoughtfully, "You could be right, I suppose."

▶ *over*

according to Custom

THOUGH combine harvesters and modern farming methods have seen many harvest customs die out, one or two still survive. In the Devon towns of Exeter and Honiton a smaller Lammas Fair takes place. The word Lammas comes from the Anglo-Saxon *hlafmaesse,* a ceremony during which a loaf made from the first wheat of the season was offered to the church. Corn dollies, now freely available in craft shops, were also a harvest custom. They were made from the last sheaf reaped and kept in barns to preserve the spirit of the crop and to ensure the next year's fertility.

"After all, Rod isn't the man who'd want a girl to go out with him out of gratitude! Mind you, we're all going to miss him and not only for what he does," Linda added thoughtfully, "He's so good with people and he never loses his cool."

"That's true. He always knows how to handle a crisis," Veronica said. "It will be . . . kind of strange without him."

And it was.

Maybe, Veronica thought, it was just chance. But it seemed as if all sorts of little things went wrong that had never gone wrong before. And people who had not clashed, seemed to irritate, disrupting the atmosphere.

"It's not been the same since Rod went away," one of the youth leaders said once. "He could charm blood out of a stone, and good temper from the worst moaners!"

But as Veronica said to him, they'd just have to manage.

"After all," she insisted, "we were working on it before he joined us."

And once, when she'd gone home for the weekend and talked to her parents about it, her dad said sagely:

"It's a fact of life that we never really realise what anybody is or what they've done — until they've gone away."

One thing Veronica was thankful for, was that her parents hadn't asked her any personal questions about Rod, or commented on his sudden reappearance in her life beyond saying how nice it was she'd had a chance to thank him again!

OF course, she acknowledged that she missed Rod, as everyone else did at the club. But she told herself it was a relief to be free of anxiety, and thankful she didn't have to face a crisis — and perhaps hurt him.

And when she ran into a former boyfriend, back in town on a visit, she did wonder what she'd ever seen in such a show-off, and found herself musing on the difference between him and Rod. She said as much to Linda.

"It's no good now," Linda said bluntly. "Rod's gone for good, that's very evident, so you've burned your boats."

"Oh, Linda," Veronica said crossly. "Don't jump to conclusions. Of course I miss him, and so does everyone. But that doesn't mean . . ."

"Of course not," Linda said soothingly. "You've been overworking. Why not go home for an extra weekend? The cows and sheep always seem to do something for you!"

▶ *164*

Some thirty years have passed since floods seriously damaged the village of Lynmouth in Devon. Today this picturesque spot is a great favourite with visitors who delight in the beautiful thatched cottages that wind their way down the steep slopes that lead to the harbour.

LYNMOUTH, Devon : J CAMPBELL KERR

So, on an impulse, Veronica rang home and said she was feeling a bit tired and would be coming that weekend.

It was always good to go back to the old stone farmhouse where she'd grown up; to go walking and riding, to help with the harvest and the animals.

Not, she told herself as the train had rumbled through the mountains, that she'd ever want to go back there to live. She loved her job and her life, but she also loved the feeling of her roots in the background, always there, always strong and sturdy.

"It's always good to know you still come back home to lick your wounds," her father said.

"Who said anything about licking wounds." Veronica laughed — not very convincingly. "I'm just worn out at work."

"Anyway, it's lovely to see you," her mother told her with a hug. "How are things going with the club building?"

After supper, Veronica produced the plans and pictures she'd brought to show them. She pointed out the stage at one end, where the wood her father sent had been used.

Going Home

THE hills lie silent with snow at the peak,
   In the valley beyond, the solace I seek.
Breath on air, feet crunching in snow,
Home I go to the haven below.

There in the distance, smoke rises high
From a cluster of chimney-pots, outlined against sky.
Soon I'll be home, invigorated, reborn,
Where a warm welcome waits on this crisp Christmas morn.

— *Barbara Cheshire*

It was when she had fetched the pictures of the first play they were rehearsing, and the designs for the costumes, that her mother went out to make a cuppa.

"D'you think she's getting bored?" she asked her dad.

"Of course not." He laughed. "You know what a teacoholic she is — and she's so pleased you've come for an extra weekend . . ." He listened suddenly. "Ah, that'll be Sam about the sheep — won't be a minute."

Veronica squatted on the floor, arranging her pictures in order, with the one of herself on top.

"Well, Mum," she said when the door opened, "how d'you like your daughter in a crinoline?" she added, without looking up.

"I bet you look marvellous."

"Ohhh!" For just a second, Veronica thought she was dreaming . . . or seeing things. But nothing so substantial as six feet of Roderick Macrae could be mistaken for a dream!

HOW . . . how on earth did you get here?" Veronica stammered incoherently, as he just stood in the doorway, smiling.

"Well, I just happened to be passing this way on holiday, popped in to say hello to your parents. And when they said you'd be here this weekend by lucky chance, I thought it'd be nice to say hello before moving on."

"W . . . w . . . where are you moving on to?" Veronica asked.

"I don't know yet," he said, and now he was laughing outright. "It all depends.

"Oh," he said, walking over to her and flopping down on the carpet beside her. "These are the pics. for the show?" He picked them up, went through them one by one as casually as if they'd only met the other day.

Afterwards, Veronica realised it must have been a full half-hour before he asked her suddenly, "Missed me?"

He put his hand under her chin and forced her to look at him. And then, as bells started to ring in her ears and the whole world seemed to be whirring, Veronica knew how much, how very much, she *had* missed him and longed for him.

"Yes, Rod," she said, knowing now she had not been mistaken, for the love in his eyes glowed. "Oh yes . . ."

"Thank heavens for that," he murmured fervently. Then he put his arms round her. "Thank heavens it worked."

It was only after an ecstatic interval, that Veronica asked him abruptly:

"What did you mean, thanking heavens for something working, Roderick Macrae . . . ?" And suddenly she knew by his uncontrollable laughter, "All that talk about happening to be here was a load of rubbish, wasn't it?"

"That's right," he said unabashed. "You see, that night I lost my head and kissed you so wildly, I saw the expression in your eyes. It was a terrible shock, Veronica." He stroked her hair fondly. "I could see just what you were thinking, that you didn't care for me in that way, but that you were —" he shivered momentarily "— in my debt."

It was after that, he explained, that he knew he had to go away, to give her the chance to see whether she missed him. So he'd volunteered to deputise for someone in the South who was off sick.

"I thought that if my ruse didn't work then I really would go to a new area. But I hoped . . . and I took your mum and dad into my confidence. They promised to let me know if ever there were any signs you might be missing me more . . . more than a little!"

"And *they* asked you to come this weekend?" Veronica breathed wonderingly.

"That's right. They said you'd told them you were worn out at work but they thought that was unlikely as you had always been a glutton for work. And so . . ." His voice suddenly changed. "Veronica, you're not angry with me . . . I was so afraid of losing you . . . so afraid perhaps even a parting wouldn't . . . wouldn't help."

She kissed him wildly.

"Oh, bless you for your wisdom, Rod. I might never have realised. I've been such a fool."

"Perish the thought!" He laughed. "Not a fool. Just a human being, love. Shall I tell your mum and dad we're ready for a celebration!" □

W HEN'S Derek picking you up, dear?"
   Pulling on her gloves, Mrs Palmer stood framed in the sitting-
   room doorway and sent an encouraging look at the slim girl
curled in the armchair.

"Around two, Mum," Christine answered. "His parents are
expecting us about three."

Giving an anxious look at the sunburst clock above the fireplace, Mrs
Palmer said.

"I'd better get down to the hall and lend a hand for the pensioners'
party. Hope you've a nice time, Christine. Don't worry. I'm sure
everything will be fine."

by
RUTH SINCLAIR

FROM THIS DAY FORWARD

Left alone, the girl didn't look as though she shared her mother's confidence. She had already met Mrs Strang, because one day when she happened to be in town, Derek suggested the three of them have lunch together.

It had turned out a rather fraught affair, for Mrs Strang on first acquaintance seemed as reserved as her son . . .

Even before Christine had ever set eyes on him, his reputation had gone before him in the office where she had worked for the past three months.

"Wait till you meet Derek Strang," Lena told her one morning. "He's quite something."

"Don't tell me the auditors are coming in again." One of the bookkeepers groaned. "You won't have time to moon over Derek, Christine. You'll be far too busy answering all their queries, or digging out missing receipts and invoices.

"They're all far too efficient, these fellows. Talk about going through everything with a fine-tooth comb!"

★　　★　　★　　★

It was several days after the auditors descended on the office before Christine had an opportunity to see the famed Mr Strang whom the girls in the pool had dubbed "The Mystery Man."

He certainly seemed to be dedicated to his work and to solving difficult financial problems, and plainly had neither the time nor the inclination to waste chatting up the female staff.

"Maybe you'll make him sit up, Christine," her friend, Lena, suggested. "Surely any man with eyes in his head would notice when you're around!"

"Thanks for the vote of confidence." She laughed, flushing at the outspoken praise. "But I'm not really interested in breaking down Derek's Strang's defences."

"Just wait till you've seen him. He's definitely the best-looking man in the whole organisation — and make the most of any chance you get. The auditors only stay here as long as it takes to check the records — and us, in the bargain. Then they go back to their own offices till the next foray."

The morning Derek strode into their office, everyone fell silent. After a brief, "Good morning," he headed straight for the head bookkeeper's desk.

A few words were spoken, then Christine to her trepidation heard her name being called, and the supervisor was waving her over.

"If you'd just have a look at this, Christine."

After the briefest of introductions, Derek said, "I believe you've been keeping these records since you came, Miss Palmer."

"Yes. Is there something wrong?"

He gave a quick shake of his dark head.

"Not a thing. But it seems to me all this information could be kept like this, rather than the old way." He pointed to a ledger with his pen. "It should take you less time, and all the more accurate. I'll check up before I leave to see if you've managed to grasp it."

"I have seen this system before," she said icily, annoyed at the implication she might be a trifle slow on the uptake. "I don't expect any difficulties changing over to it now."

LUNCHING with Lena later, she exclaimed, "So that's the mystery man the girls rave over. I found him supercilious, over-bearing, probably full of his own conceit."

Lena regarded her with a faint smile curving her lips.

"I think maybe you protest too much. Nobody's ever found him anything other than polite and courteous — maybe a bit distant, but that could be sour grapes because he hasn't gone overboard for any of us. More's the pity."

"Let's change the subject," Christine implored.

She was tired of hearing about Derek Strang, the mystery man, from nine in the morning until five o'clock. Surely there could be some respite during the lunch hour?

The new system might mean less work later on, but the changeover from the old method involved Christine in a considerable amount of copying. She was so intent on getting everything right up to date in case the auditors wanted to check them again, that she worked on after hours — despite the head bookkeeper's protest that there was no need for all this haste.

"I'll only be another hour, Miss Martin, and I'd feel better if I knew I had everything sorted out."

"Well, don't work too long," the supervisor said with an approving smile at the girl. "We want to keep you, Christine, not sicken you with overwork."

It was pouring with rain when she finally emerged through the swing doors, and as luck or fate would have it, two of the auditors followed on the next turn of the doors.

One, of course, was Derek Strang. It *would* be, she thought in annoyance.

"Jump in," he offered pleasantly as he opened the door of his car, "before you get soaked."

"No, it's all right. I'm just going to the library at the end of the road. Thanks all the same."

Determinedly Christine put up her umbrella and headed away from them, aware she was leaving behind two somewhat puzzled young men.

Seconds later, the car passed her with Derek at the wheel. His colleague, a chatty type called Mark Ames, gave her a cheery wave and she hoisted the umbrella higher at him before hurrying on.

She knew exactly the conclusions the girls would arrive at if she'd accepted.

"Smart thing," Lena would probably say in approval, imagining she had purposefully left at the same time as the auditors. Christine found her cheeks were burning partly through embarrassment and partly

169

because of the stinging rain that was getting harder by the minute.

Then she was in the shelter of the library where she changed some records and a book for her mother. Once outside again the prospect of queueing up at the nearest bus stop in this weather was daunting enough to make her look hopefully for a taxi.

Instead she saw Derek Strang standing at the open door of his car, obviously waiting for her.

"Come on," he insisted. "You've probably been working late because I changed the books' layout. The least I can do is offer to run you home, or wherever you're going. Get in."

Nonplussed, she did as she was told, and in silence he got in the driver's side and turned the ignition key.

"Where?"

"Ferris Avenue, if you're sure. What happened to Mr Ames?"

"I just delivered him at his bus stop, as usual. He goes right out of town."

Apart from that, there was little conversation on the journey home, apart from the odd polite question about how she liked the new arrangement, and her stilted replies. After that, the lift proceeded for the most part in silence.

"This is my street," she said at length. "And the rain's stopped. I can walk from here. Thank you very much for giving me a lift."

"My pleasure."

He sat in the car, waiting till she reached the front door safely, but when she half turned, he started up the engine again and drove off.

ONE morning sometime later his car drew up as she was on her way to the office, and this time it would have been silly not to accept the proffered lift. This time just before they reached the office, he asked if she might be free one evening as there was quite a good comedy on in the theatre.

Christine thoroughly enjoyed the play, laughing in all the right places, but apart from a faint smile or two, Derek didn't appear to find it particularly funny. She had made up her mind by the end of the evening that he must have found her company boring, and probably wouldn't ask to take her out again.

However, when the car pulled up in front of her house, he thanked her and hoped they might do it again sometime.

"Perhaps," she said, getting out the car, a little disappointed that he

▶ *172*

Once a thriving shipbuilding centre, the royal burgh of Burntisland stands on the shores of the Firth of Forth. Industry still makes a major contribution to the town with its important aluminium plant. Further up the coast lie the fishing villages that make this part of Fife such a popular area with day visitors and holidaymakers.

BURNTISLAND, Fife : J CAMPBELL KERR

had not even put his arm round her. He certainly was a mystery just as the girls said, but maybe the truth was that he didn't find any of them attractive, including herself.

Somewhat soberly she went indoors, and to her mother's query simply dismissed it as, "Quite a good play. It was quite entertaining."

"You should have asked him in for a cup of coffee before he went home. Where is home, anyway?"

"Oh, he's in digs somewhere," she said carelessly. "It saves him from travelling down to Ayr every night and back in the mornings. That's where his folk stay."

A few days later, he dropped by her desk to say his mother was to be in town and he wondered if she would care to join them for lunch.

"Well, if you're sure, Derek, that would be nice."

Mrs Strang turned out to be in her mid-fifties, very well turned out, and obviously had been having her hair done in an expensive salon. She chatted easily and complimented Christine on her fine complexion.

"Lucky you, you don't need to bother with much make-up with a skin like that."

"Sometimes I do," Christine admitted. "I burn quickly if there's too much sunshine."

Though the talk flowed back and forth and even Derek seemed a little more forthcoming than normal, Christine had the feeling that Mrs Strang was not altogether happy about her son's interest in herself.

Back in the office, Lena was agog to hear how she had got on.

"To tell you the truth, Mrs Strang seems almost as reserved as her son. We talked but there seemed to be some kind of undercurrent I didn't understand."

Before they had parted, Mrs Strang said, "Of course you must come down to see us in Ayr. Derek must bring your sometime."

But although he asked her out on several occasions after that, he seemed to have forgotten about his mother's invitation.

ONE Saturday when he had arranged to take her for a spin in the car, for her choice of destination she suggested St Andrews.

"You wouldn't like to go to Ayr, Christine?"

"Some other time maybe. I just fancy a trip to the east coast for a change — unless of course you'd prefer . . ."

"No," he said quickly. "St Andrews is fine."

They had a meal there and after that he drove out to the beach where they sat looking out at the choppy water from the comfort of the car.

"Did you want to explore the town?" he asked, putting an arm round her shoulder.

"Maybe later. It's cosy in here."

He bent his head and kissed her then, a long slow kiss.

A few seconds later she moved away.

"I know so little about you, Derek," she said. "You know, you've a reputation in our firm for being a man of mystery."

He gave a wry smile.

"You surprise me — and then you don't. I can see why your

girlfriends might say that. I'm really not one for wholesale dating. In fact, Christine, I was married. My wife and I went through the university here together and we lived in St Andrews for another year after I qualified."

She pulled away gently to gaze at him squarely.

"But you stay in digs, don't you? Your wife . . . ?"

"Anna died three years ago, just after our baby was born."

Christine sat aghast at the revelation of how much misery and grief he had known, and understanding flooded her. Small wonder he had seemed so reserved and withdrawn, and had found precious little to laugh about that night at the theatre.

"I'm so sorry. It must have been dreadful for you — to lose the one you love like that — so early in life."

She had put her hand on his arm and felt the shudder that went through him as he tried to overcome his grief.

"What about your baby, Derek?"

"My mother has brought Kitty up ever since — she loves her dearly."

And probably lives in dread that someone will take Kitty away from her, Christine thought, remembering that look of fear she had seen on Mrs Strang's face. She understood so well now so many things.

"I'm sorry," Derek was saying. "This was supposed to be a day's happy outing for you. I've no right to pour out my troubles to you."

"Who else would you tell them to?" she asked, tenderly enfolding him in a warm embrace.

CHRISTINE got up from the armchair and crossed to the window so she could see his car when it turned the corner.

Today she was going at last to the house in Ayr to make friends with a three-year-old little girl who was too young to know what a grievous loss she had sustained.

There were two future in-laws she would have to show that in marrying Derek she had no intention of breaking up their happy life as doting grandparents. Surely they could work out some arrangement about Kitty that wouldn't leave any bruised hearts in its wake?

She caught sight of the car then and hastened to collect her packages, toys for Kitty and flowers for her gran. Then she pulled the front door firmly behind her and ran to meet him.

"Well?" he asked, once she was settled beside him and the packages stowed on the back seat. "Have you made up your mind? Are you going to marry me?"

"I think I made up my mind the day you changed the bookkeeping system."

"You still haven't answered my question, and this car's not moving an inch till I have the right one."

"Yes, Derek. Of course it's yes." □

Printed and published in Great Britain by D. C. Thomson & Co., Ltd., Dundee, Glasgow, London and Manchester.
© D. C. Thomson & Co., Ltd., 1987.
ISBN 0-85116-404-8